GLORY

SPRING HARVEST PRAISE 2010

COPYRIGHT & PHOTOCOPYING

ACKNOWLEDGEMENTS

Music type-setting and new arrangements by David Ball
Design & Layout by Wildfire Studio
Printed by Halcyon

Published and distributed by
Elevation, 14 Horsted Square, Uckfield,
East Sussex, TN22 1QG, UK.

Part of the Memralife Group, Registered Charity number 1126997, a Company limited by guarantee, registered in England and Wales, number 6667924.

Registered Office: 14 Horsted Square, Uckfield,
East Sussex. TN22 1QG

Spring Harvest wishes to acknowledge and thank the following people for their help in the compilation and production of this song book: Andreana Arganda, Leigh Barnard, Mark Beswick, Pete Broadbent, Janet Cole, Andrew Crookall, Sam Hargreaves, Nick Herbert, Denise Hooper, Cheryl Jenkinson, Karen Martin, Trevor Michael, David Peacock, Ruth Perrett, Jo Petch, Sue Rinaldi, Joy Townhill and Rachel Whitney .

Thank you to Marie Birkinshaw, Mark Earey Nick Harding, Sam Hargreaves, Gerard Kelly and Ruth Sermon for liturgy contributions.

ISBN 978-1-899788-70-5

CONTENTS

Songs are listed in the order of first line, not title. In a few cases, alphabetical ordering of songs has been changed slightly, in order to ensure that page turns are not needed in any two-page songs.

The words edition of this songbook is also available in Braille and giant print

INDEX

Song titles differing from first lines are in italics

ALL BECAUSE OF YOU

David Ostby

D
A
F♯m7
am be-cause You are,
I live be-cause You live,
Gmaj7
D
A
I love be-cause You loved me first.
1.
F♯m7
Gmaj7
D.C.
D
2.4.
F♯m7
Gmaj7
D.S.
3.,5.
F♯m7
I
Gmaj7
play 1st time only
D
D/F♯

Mid section

(After D.S.S.)

Bm7 A F♯m7 G2

I'm a-live cos You're a-live, I'm a-live cos You're a-live,

Bm7 A F♯m7 G2 *(Fine)*

I'm a-live cos You're a-live in me.

G A/G Bm/G A/G *D.S.S. al Fine*

Sing,

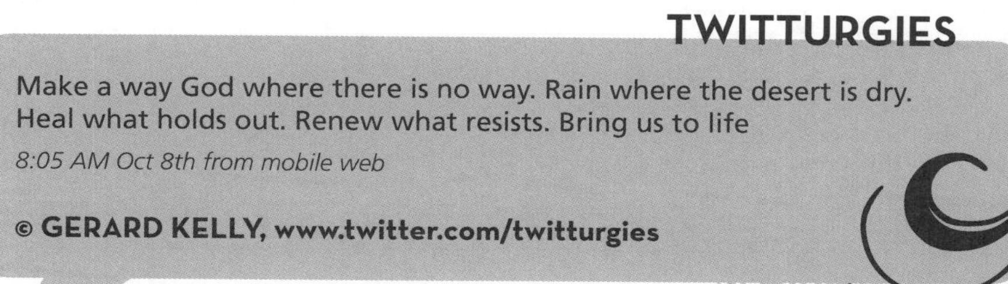

TWITTURGIES

Make a way God where there is no way. Rain where the desert is dry. Heal what holds out. Renew what resists. Bring us to life

8:05 AM Oct 8th from mobile web

2. A LIMITLESS MAJESTY

(You are greater)

Ben Jones
& Sue Rinaldi

This song is recorded on the Spring Harvest 'Glory - New Songs 2010' album

Chorus
D F♯7 D Bm
true. You are great - er, You are
true. none more grace - ful, none more
G Gm 1.,3. D Dmaj7
high - er, I see; have all of me. There's
pow'r - ful than You; take all of
2. D F♯7 D.C. (v.2) 4. D Dmaj7 D.S.
me. me.
5. D F♯7 Gmaj7 Tag D
me. A heart that's drip - ping with grace, a
Gmaj7 A D
rit.
Fa - ther that longs to em - brace, mer - cy that makes me com - plete.

3. ALL I ONCE HELD DEAR

(Knowing You)

Graham Kendrick

This song is recorded on the Spring Harvest 'Journey - Live Worship 2009' album

A PRAYER OF CONFESSION

Lord Jesus Christ,
We are sorry that we have filled the voids of our hearts with our own darkness instead of with your light. We confess that we have conformed to this world, and not been transformed by the renewal of our minds. Cleanse us and fill us afresh with your love and peace. We ask this by the power of your Holy Spirit, that we might live to your glory and praise. **Amen.**

4. ALL THE HEAVENS PRAISE

(Great and glorious)

Capo 5(Am)

Jo Petch

This song is recorded on the Spring Harvest 'Glory - New Songs 2010' album

B♭(F)
F(C)
C(G)
'Ho - ly is Your name, ho - ly is Your name'.
Chorus
B♭(F)
F(C)
Am(Em)
Great and glo - ri - ous, You reign, You reign.
Dm(Am)
B♭(F)
F(C)
Last time to Coda
All the hea - vens and the earth cry out in praise.
1.
C(G)
2.,4.
C(G)
D.S.
3.
C(G)
Mid section
B♭(F)
There's no one high - er, no

C(G) B♭(F) C(G)
one greater, no one is more powerful. There's no
1.
B♭(F) C(G) B♭/D(F) C(G)
one wiser, no one stronger than You. There's no
2.
Gm(Dm) C(G) B♭(F)
one wiser, no one stronger than You. Our God.
D.S. al Coda
Coda
C(G) C(G)
There's no one like You, God.
B♭maj7(F) C(G) B♭maj7(F)
There's no one like You, God. There's no

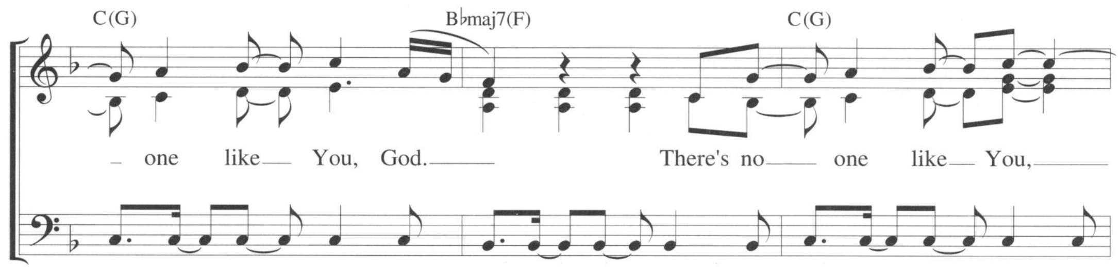

GRACIOUS GOD

Gracious God, we are your church. Help us to see with your eyes.
May your church be filled with your vision, and clear in our message.

Gracious God, we are your church. Help us to see with your eyes.
May your church be a light in the darkness, and take real love to hard places.

Gracious God, we are your church. Help us to see with your eyes.
May your church be bold in our mission, and motivated by change.

Gracious God, we are your church. Help us to see with your eyes.

5. ALL THE ROOM WAS HUSHED AND STILL

(Love each other)

Graham Kendrick

This song is recorded on the Spring Harvest 'Journey - Live Worship 2009' album

Gm(Em)
F(D)
E♭(C) E♭2(C)
this is what I want the world — to see who it is — you fol-low.' —
B♭(G)
Chorus
F/A(D)
Gm(Em)
'Love each oth - er, one a-no - ther, love each o - ther in the
E♭2(C)
B♭(G)
F/A(D)
way that I — have loved you.' 'Walk to-ge - ther, and what-e - ver — comes,
Gm(Em)
1.
E♭(C)
E♭2(C)
love each o - ther in the way that I — have loved you.' —
D.S.
2.
D.S.S. to repeat chorus
Cm/E♭(Am) Gm(Em)
F(D)
E♭(C)
B♭(G)
2. Let the room — way that I — have loved you.' —

6. AS WE COME INTO YOUR PRESENCE

(Because of Your love)

Paul Baloche
& Brenton Brown

G/B
C2
Dsus4
because of Your love
our hearts are clean.
G/B
C2
Dsus4
G/B
C2
Dsus4
We lift You up
with songs of free-
G/B
C2
Dsus4
A7/C♯
C2
-dom,
for-e-ver we're
changed
D
G(no3rd)
G/B
C2
Dsus4
because of Your
love.
Yeah,
G
G/B
C2
Dsus4
1.
D.C.
To end
G
G
yeah.
As we

7. AT THE CROSS, WHERE JESUS SUFFERED

(Merciful)

Graham Kendrick

D G Em Em/A D
sting of wrongs re - mem - bered, no more mea - sur - ing my loss.
good the ill we suf - fer, works all things in - to Love's plan.
be the thanks I of - fer: I will to - tal - ly for - give.
Chorus
G F♯m D G Bm A D/F♯
For my Fa - ther in heav - ven showed mer - cy to me. How can
G D/F♯ G A Bm Em Em/A Bm7
I not be mer - ci - ful when God's been mer - ci - ful to me, God's been
Em Em/A
1.,2.
D Dsus4 D
D.C.
3.
D
D.S.
mer - ci - ful to me. 2. I'll not me. For my
3. Ho - ly
4.
D Dsus4 D Em/A D
me.

8. BE LIFTED HIGH ABOVE THE HEAVENS

(Ring out)

Tim Sanders

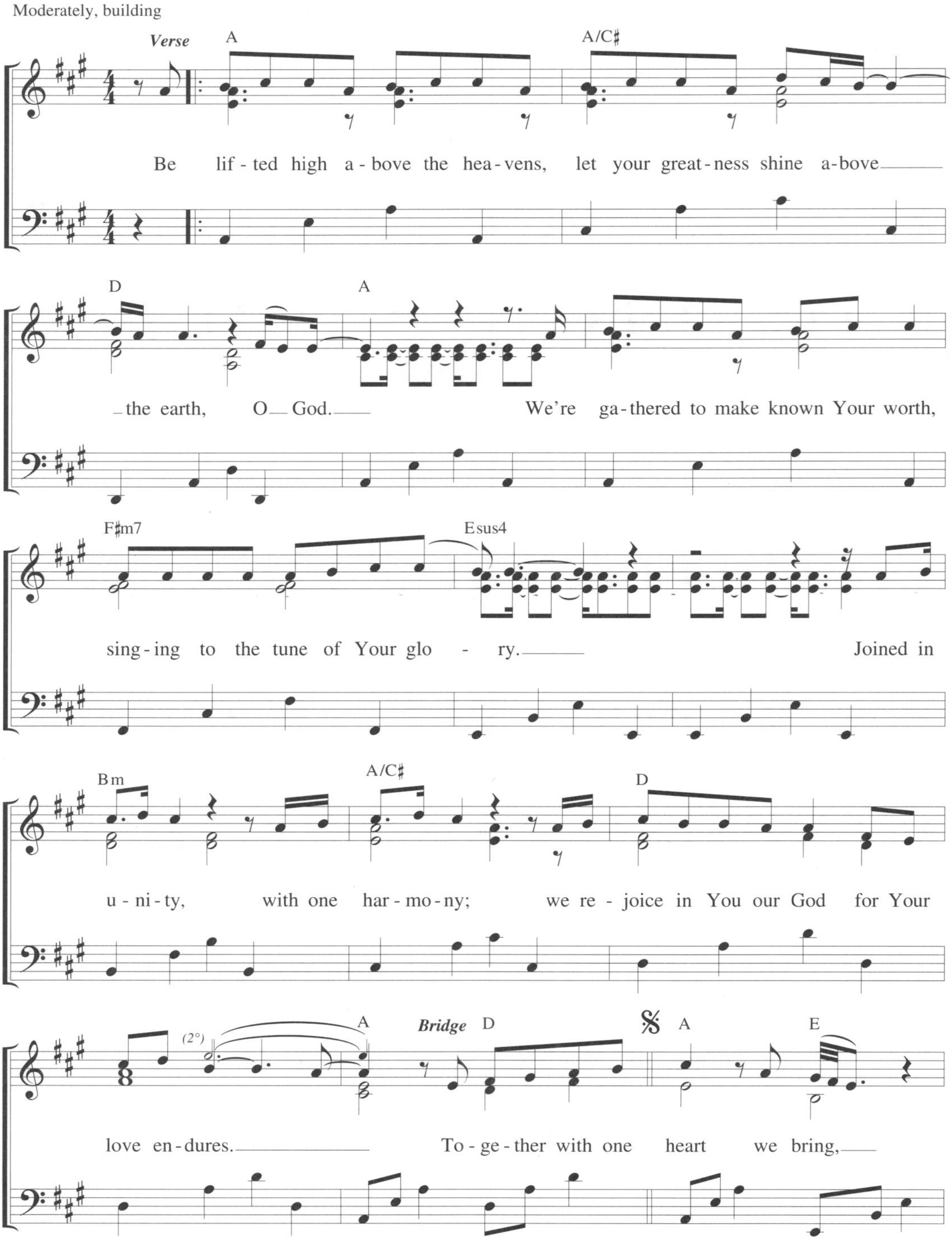
Moderately, building
Verse
A
A/C♯
Be lif - ted high a - bove the hea - vens, let your great - ness shine a - bove
D
A
the earth, O God. We're ga - thered to make known Your worth,
F♯m7
Esus4
sing - ing to the tune of Your glo - ry. Joined in
Bm
A/C♯
D
u - ni - ty, with one har - mo - ny; we re - joice in You our God for Your
(2°)
A
Bridge
D
A
E
love en - dures. To - ge - ther with one heart we bring,

A/C♯ D A E Chorus A/C♯ D2
u-ni-ted as one voice we'll sing Your praise. Ev-'ry
A E A/C♯ D2 A E
tongue will con-fess: "You're great, and great-ly to be praised". One God,
Last time to Coda
A/C♯ D2 A E 1. A/C♯ D2
one King, let the u-ni-verse ring out Your name.
Esus4 2. A/C♯ D2 Esus4 Mid section A
Be Glo-ry, ho-nour, praise-and pow-er
D F♯m 1. D
be to our God for-e-ver. Glo-ry, ho-nour, praise and pow-er be to our God for-e-ver.

2.
D
A
D
be to our God for - e - ver.
For - e - ver.
F♯m
D
A
For - e - ver.
D
F♯m
D
For - e - ver.
D.S. al Coda
Coda
A
D
A
E
A/C♯
D2
To - ge - ther with one
u - ni - verse ring out one God, one King, let the
A
E
A/C♯
D2
Esus4
u - ni - verse ring out Your name.

ALL-AGE WORSHIP BEAUTIFUL TIME

Steve & Jo Squires

All-age worship is a beautiful opportunity for the whole family of God to come together to worship the God they love... and yet often it doesn't feel all that 'beautiful', many even avoid it! What does it take to create a beautiful time of genuine worship for everyone?

Picture if you will: an idyllic Christmas (bear with me here...): there are times when the whole family will sit down together, enjoy good food and one another's company. There will also be times when 'grown-ups' sit and have a coffee or mulled-wine (punctuated perhaps by some 'resting of eyes') while the littler ones play with their new toys (or the boxes they came in!). The teens are trying out their new 'gadget', or helping Dad to use his. In my family, there's usually a new board game to play together too.

This is a beautiful time... there are periods of 'different ages' doing 'different things', but everyone celebrates together, in the same place. That 'togetherness' is so important, and so valuable.

This is a model BIG Ministries try and practice in all-age worship. We're not a group of adults watching the kids play with their toys. Neither are we a group of kids watching the adults have their time. But rather we share 'togetherness', everyone engaged simultaneously, although not always in the same activity. We enjoy each others' company and worship together.

All-age worship, in it's most effective form, is a totally unique and exciting type of worship requiring lots of creativity and some out-of-the-box thinking!

Here's a brief checklist of things to think about when you're planning and leading a time of all-age worship:

Planning the 'beautiful time'...

Look at each individual item, and the programme as a whole, and think about these 3 things...

Is it appropriate?

- Is what I'm planning simple and clear? (it should be). Remember 'simple and clear' doesn't mean we have to stay clear of big concepts or themes.
- Is it childish, embarrassing, or patronising? (it should not be).

  For example, look at our language...
  NOT: 'Let's come before the Lord in penitence for our transgressions'
  NOR: 'Now we're going to say sorry for the naughty things we've done'
  BUT simple, uncomplicated language that doesn't patronise like: 'We're going to spend a bit of time saying sorry to God for things we've done wrong.'

Is it interactive?

- Is it moving quickly enough? (variety is crucial).
  - As a general rule, aim for each activity to last NO LONGER than 7 minutes.
- Interaction helps everyone engage, learn and worship.
  - Interaction could be in the form of: movement; sign-language; singing; using our senses; interactive stories (like '10 BIG Bible Stories'); talking in small groups; making things and so much more...
  - Always give people a subtle 'get-out' clause, never force interaction!

As an example...

It could be that there are different 'interactive' things happening all at the same time. So, perhaps a traditional hymn about God's amazing creation is sung, during which there's a creative, colouring activity or even digital photos being taken outside and then shared later. All these different things simultaneously facilitate lots of people in worship.

Is it inclusive?

- Does any activity alienate people, if so can we change it?

A note for those leading the beautiful time...

Remember you are leading worship:

ALWAYS be enthusiastic and enjoy it (still being yourself!)

NEVER be apologetic for what you're leading - people won't want to join in!

NEVER separate items with lines like: 'now we're going to sing a children's song' or 'here's one for the Oldies' which immediately alienates everyone else.

So... let's keep on exploring how we can lead relevant and engaging all-age worship, as if we're a 'real life family' with all the sacrifice and compromise that brings. And remember... it's all about God,and leading people in worship of HIM!

Steve & Jo Squires

www.bigministries.co.uk

Available from all good Christian retailers, iTunes & www.essentialchristian.com

9. BEFORE THE WORLD WAS MADE

(Glory to God forever)

Steve Fee
& Vicky Beeching

Capo 4(G)

Moderately

This song is recorded on the Spring Harvest 'Glory - New Songs 2010' album

Chorus
E(C)
B(G)
F♯(D)
G♯m(Em)
Last time to Coda
Glo-ry to God,
glo-ry to God,
glo-ry to God for-e-ver.
1.,3.,5.
2.
Yeah.
D.C. (v.2)
4.,6.
Mid section
Take my life and let it be all for You and for Your glo-ry,
take my life and let it be Yours.
1.
2.
D.S.
Coda
We sing

10. BEHOLD, A BROKEN WORLD

WE ARE CHOSEN

People: We are chosen by the King of kings,
Leader: you are loved with an everlasting love.

People: Not for our looks -
Leader: though he sees you as beautiful,

People: Not for our good works -
Leader: though he cherishes every gift you give back to him.

People: Not because we're strong -
Leader: because his power is perfect in your weakness.

People: We belong in the family of God,
Leader: you are loved by your heavenly Father.

Amen.

11. BREATHE ON ME

Capo 3(D)

E. Hatch adpt. Darren Baird

Flowing

C/E(A) F(D) B♭2(G) Dm7(Bm)

pure, un - til my __ will __ is one with __ Thine, __ to do and to __
die, but live with __ Thee __ the per - fect __ life __ of Thine e - ter -

Gm(Em) F/A(D) C/E(A) F(D) B♭2(G) B♭2/C(G)

_ en - dure; breathe on __ me, __ Breath of __ God. _
- ni - ty; breathe on __ me, __ Breath of __ God. _

1. F(D) 2. F(D)

_ 2. Breathe on __ me, __ _

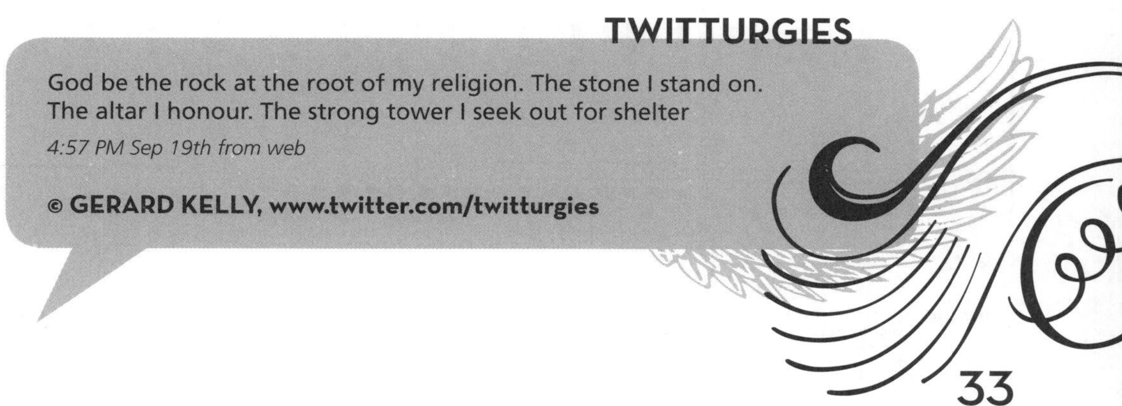

TWITTURGIES

God be the rock at the root of my religion. The stone I stand on. The altar I honour. The strong tower I seek out for shelter

4:57 PM Sep 19th from web

12. BREAK OUR HEARTS

Capo 3(D)

Vicky Beeching

Dm(Bm) C/E(A) F(D)
time for us to live the songs we sing, and
time to move out - side our com - fort zones, to
Dm(Bm) C(A) B♭(G)
turn our good in - ten - tions in - to ac - tions; to
see be - yond our church - es and our homes; to
Dm(Bm) C/E(A) F(D)
bring the kind of wor - ship You de - sire, and
change the way we think and how we spend, un -
Dm(Bm) C(A) B♭(G) Bridge Gm(Em) Dm(Bm)
(v.2)
move be - yond our self - ab - sorbed dis - tractions.
til we look like Je - sus a - gain.
The moun - tains are shak - ing,
C(A) Gm(Em) Dm(Bm) C(A) D.C.
could this be a great a - wak - en - ing?

A PRAYER FOR FAITH LIKE ABRAHAM'S

From Genesis 12.3

Faithful God,
through Abraham and his people
you blessed many nations.
Give us a faith like his
and make us, like him, a blessing to others. Amen.

BY THIS WORLD MY HEART WAS WOUNDED 13.

(Sweet Jesus)

This song is recorded on the Spring Harvest 'Glory - New Songs 2010' album

14. BY FAITH WE SEE THE HAND OF GOD

F♯m D2 A F♯m D2
stand as chil-dren of the pro-mise, we will fix our eyes on him: our
A E A F♯m D2 A A2/C♯ D2
soul's re - ward. Till the race is fin-ished and the work is done,
Last time to Coda
1.,2.
D.C.(v.3/v.5)
Bm7 D E Asus2 D/A Asus2 D/A
we'll walk by faith and not by sight.
3.
D.S. al Coda
Coda
A F♯m Bm7 D E
sight. We will sight. we'll walk by faith and not by
Ano3rd Amaj7 D/A Ano3rd Amaj7 D/A A
sight.

15. CAN YOU HEAR, THERE'S A NEW SONG

(A new hallelujah)

Michael W. Smith, Paul Baloche
& Debbie Smith

C
G
let the church a-rise;
let love
C
G
reach to the oth-er side.
A-live,
Em
C
come a-live,
Last time to Coda
G(no3rd)
C/G G
G(no3rd)
let the song a-rise.
1.
C/G G
2.
C/G G
Mid section
F
3. All the
Oh,

Am
G
(oh,)
yeah.
(yeah.)
Let the
F
Am
G
song a-rise,
(let the song a-rise,)
yeah.
(yeah.)
F
Am
G
Let the song a-rise,
(let the song a-rise.)
D.S. al Coda
Coda
C/G G
C/G G
C/G G
A-rise,
Ev-'ry
C/G G
C/G G
one sing a new hal-le-lu-jah; ev-'ry-one sing a new hal-le-lu-jah.

COME, LEARN OF GOD'S KINGDOM 16.

17. COME, SEE THE SON

Gm7(Em)
E♭(C)
F(D)
– por - trayed – in Christ, –
– who will – be - lieve –
the cross of Christ. –
in Je - sus Christ. –
1.,2.
B♭(G)
Gm7(Em)
F/A(D)
B♭(G)
Gm7(Em)
F/A(D) B♭(G)
3.,4.
1° D.S. (ch 3)
B♭(G)
Tag
E♭(C)
Come and wor - ship him, –
B♭/D(G)
Gm7(Em)
come and sing – to him, –
come and live –
E♭(C)
F(D)
1.
B♭(G)
2.
B♭(G)
– for him, –
Je - sus Christ. –

18. CREATION SINGS THE FATHER'S SONG

Keith and Kristyn Getty
& Stuart Townend

F C/E G C Chorus G
mands the new - born ba - by's cry. Hal - le - lu -
live with him e - ter - nal - ly.
glo - ry of our God and King!
Am F C/E G C G
jah! Let all cre - a - tion stand and sing: 'Hal - le - lu -
Am F C/E F C/E F C/E G
jah!' Fill the earth with songs of wor - ship, tell the won - ders of cre - a - tion's
C G/C F/C C G/C F/C C G/C F/C 1.,2. C G/C F/C D.C. 3. C
King.
2. Cre -
3. Cre -

19. DEFENDER OF THIS HEART

(Remain)

Ben Cantelon

Chorus
G
D/F♯
A
D/F♯
You are God with us, You're vic - tor - i - ous, You are strong
and migh - ty to save. For Your word stands true, there is none
like You, and when all else fades You re - main.
Em
G
D
1.,2.,4.
1° D.C. (v.2)
3.
D.S.
Last time
You are God

20. DARK BEFORE THE DAWN

(His love)

This song is recorded on the Spring Harvest 'Glory - New Songs 2010' album

Gm7(Em) Eb(C) Bb/F(G) F(D)
lay - ing down his own life to die in a - go - ny.
all he did was love us, and how did we re - pay?
all cre - a - tion sing - ing songs of li - ber - ty.
Bb/D(G) Eb(C) Bb/F(G) Gm(Em)
What a great sur - ren - der, what a great sur - ren - der,
We are now for - gi - ven, we are now for - gi - ven,
He cried: 'It is fin - ished', my heart sings: 'It's fin - ished',
Bb/D(G) Eb(C) Cm7(Am) Chorus Fsus4(D) F(D)
what a great sur - ren - der: he gave his life for me.
we are now for - gi - ven, and this is now our claim: His
once for all it's fin - ished, all hea - ven and earth a - gree.
Bb(G) Eb(C) Bb/D(G) Eb(C)
love has more than con - quered, his love has paid for

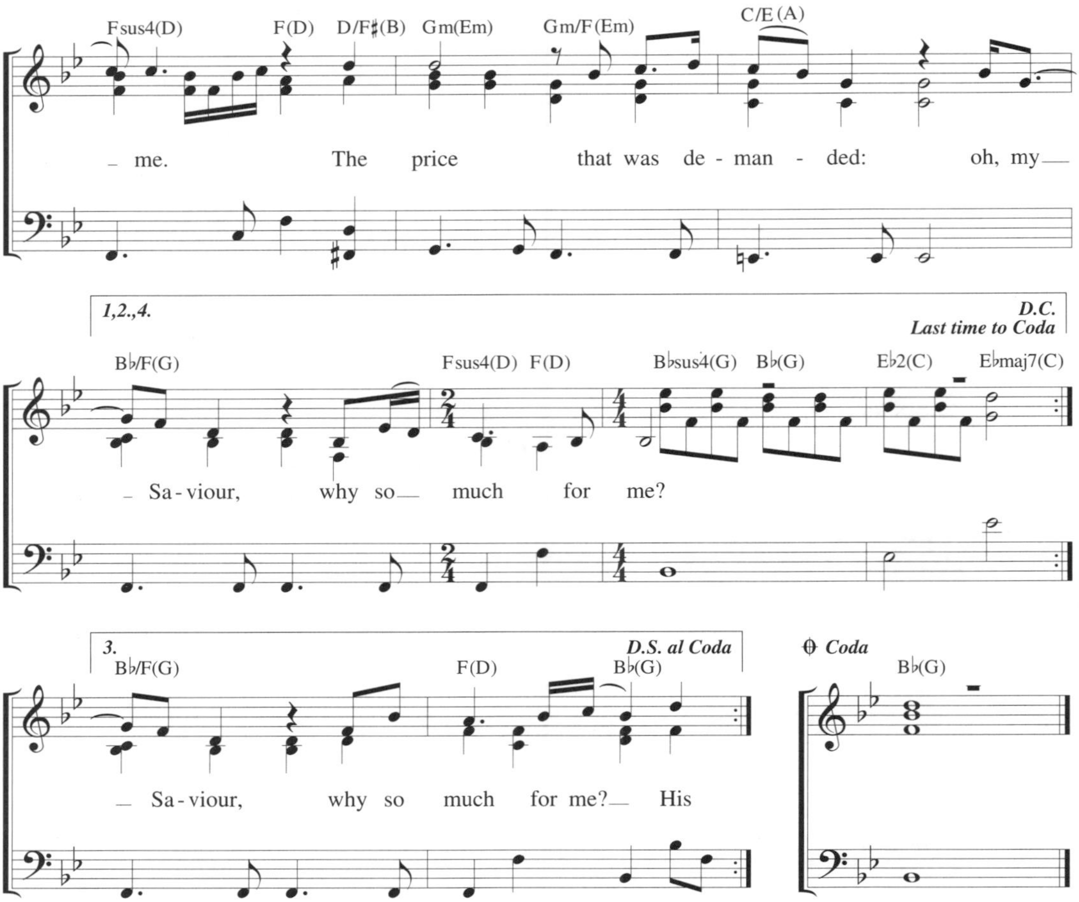

Fsus4(D) F(D) D/F♯(B) Gm(Em) Gm/F(Em) C/E(A)

_ me. The price that was de - man - ded: oh, my _

1,2.,4. D.C. *Last time to Coda*

B♭/F(G) Fsus4(D) F(D) B♭sus4(G) B♭(G) E♭2(C) E♭maj7(C)

_ Sa - viour, why so _ much for me?

3. *D.S. al Coda*

B♭/F(G) F(D) B♭(G)

_ Sa - viour, why so much for me? _ His

Coda

B♭(G)

DELIVERER, COME SET ME FREE 21.

(Deliverer)

Vicky Beeching
& Sarah MacIntosh

This song is recorded on the Spring Harvest 'Glory - New Songs 2010' album

1.
(Fine)
D.C. (v.2)
Am C G/B
of the Lord is, there is heal - ing. 2. You say the word
2.
G/B Mid section Dm Am G
there is heal - ing. Where the Spi - rit of the Lord is, there is free - dom. Where the
Dm Am G Dm
Spi - rit of the Lord is, there is hope. Where the Spi - rit of the Lord is,
Am G F
there is heal - ing. And Your blood
Dm7 Am G
is e - nough to break e - ve - ry chain. And Your blood

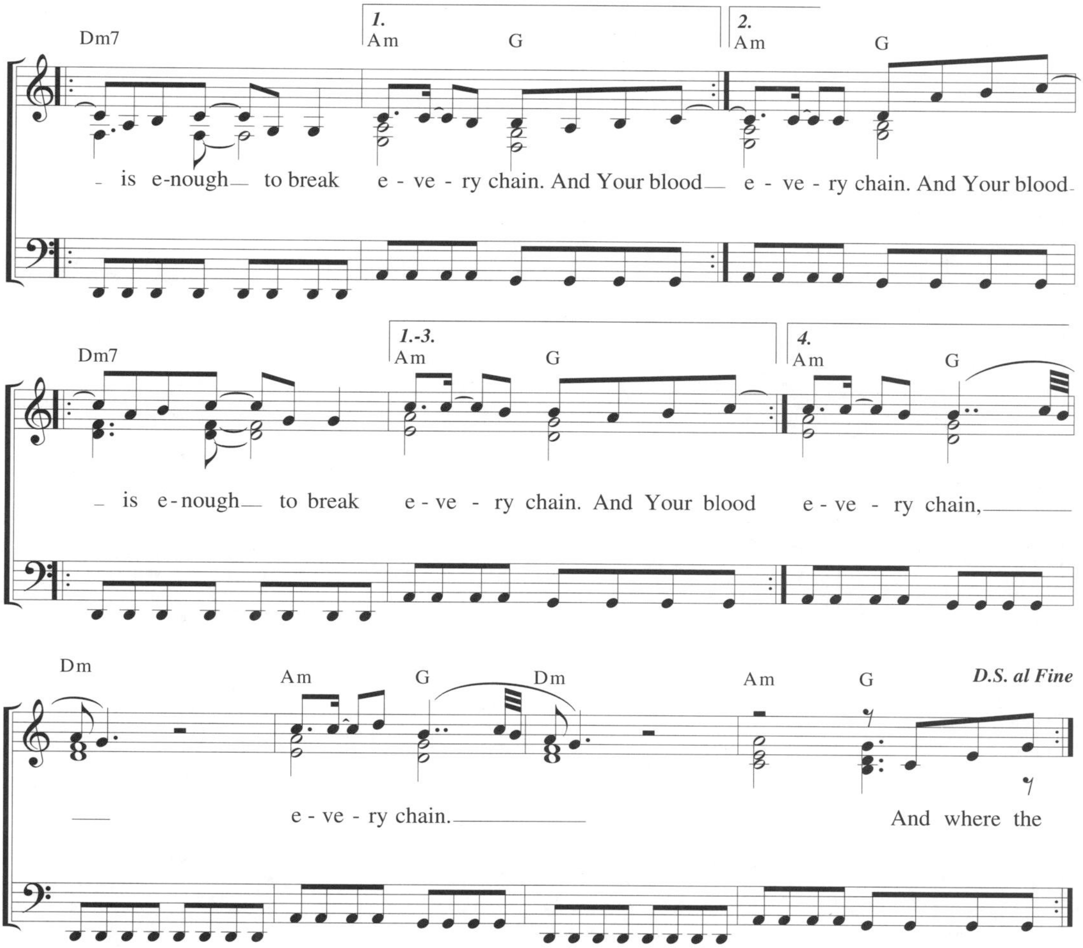

Dm7 | 1. Am G | 2. Am G

– is e-nough — to break e - ve - ry chain. And Your blood — e - ve - ry chain. And Your blood –

Dm7 | 1.-3. Am G | 4. Am G

– is e-nough — to break e - ve - ry chain. And Your blood e - ve - ry chain, —

Dm | Am G | Dm | Am G *D.S. al Fine*

— e - ve - ry chain. — And where the

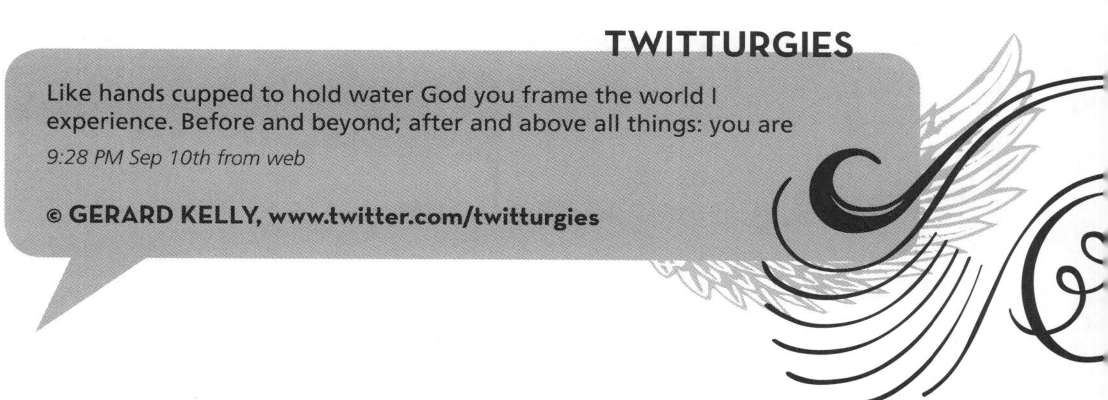

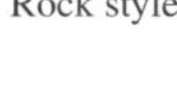

EVERLASTING GOD

(Yesterday, today and forever)

Capo 3 (D)

Rock style

Vicky Beeching

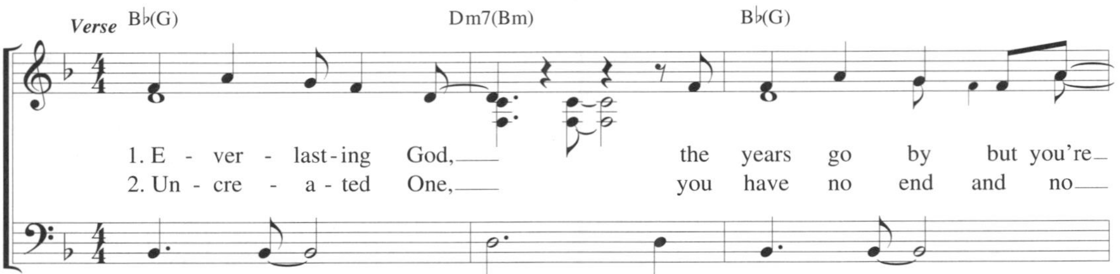

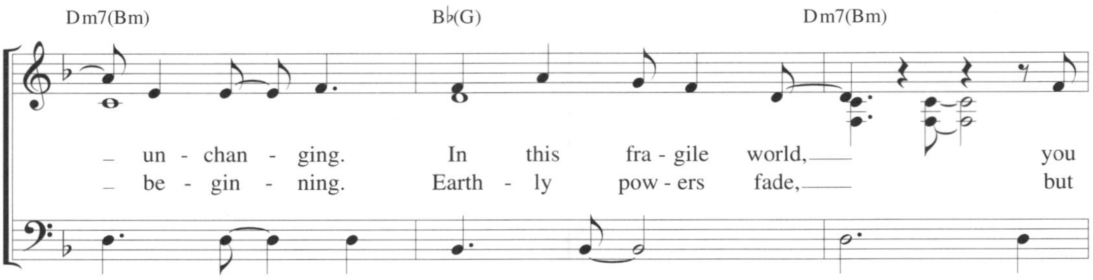

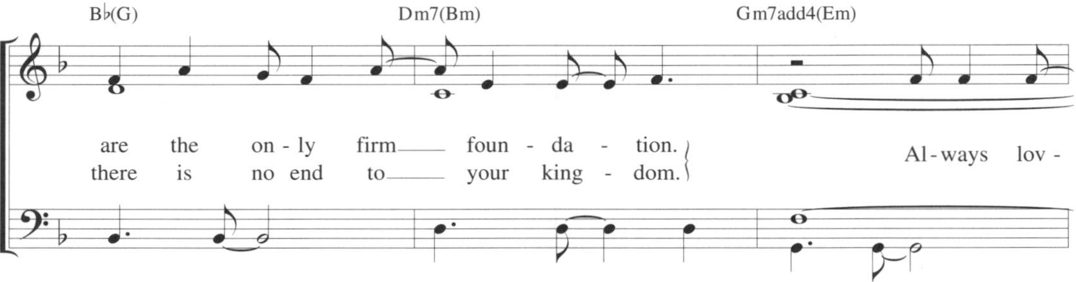

This song is recorded on the Spring Harvest 'One Hope - Live worship 2008' and 'Kids Praise Party 3' albums

Dm7(Bm) C(A)
ci - ful and good, so good.
Chorus
F/A(D) B♭(G) Dm7(Bm) C(A) F/A(D) B♭(G)
Yes - ter - day, to - day and for - e - ver, you are the same,
Dm7(Bm) C(A) F/A(D) B♭(G) Dm7(Bm) C(A)
you ne - ver change. Yes - ter - day, to - day and for - e - ver,
Last time to Coda
Gm7(Em) B♭(G) C(A) 1. F/A(D) B♭(G)
you are faith - ful and we will trust in you.
Dm7(Bm) C(A) 2. B♭(G) F/A(D)
We will trust in you,

B♭(G)
F/A(D)
we will trust in you, in you.
B♭2(G)
Bridge
F/A(D)
B♭2(G)
Yah - weh, God un - chan - ging. Yah - weh,
F/A(D)
1.
3
2.
D.S. al Coda
firm foun - da - tion. You are da - tion.
Coda
F(D)

FOREVER AND A DAY

23.

Last time to Coda
A
F♯m7
D2
Hal - le-lu - jah, Je - sus, we love Your name, for
1.
D.C.
2.
D.S.
E/G♯
E/G♯
all You've done.
all You've done. We sing
3.
E/G♯
Eadd4
Mid section
A/C♯
D2
all You've done.
And I will give You
F♯m7
Eadd4
A/C♯
D2
1.,2.
F♯m7
(small notes 2°)
Eadd4
all my praise; and I will sing of Your great name. And
3.
F♯m7
Eadd4
A/C♯
D2
F♯m7
Eadd4
A/C♯
D2
Your great name, Lord. And I will give You all my praise; and I will sing of

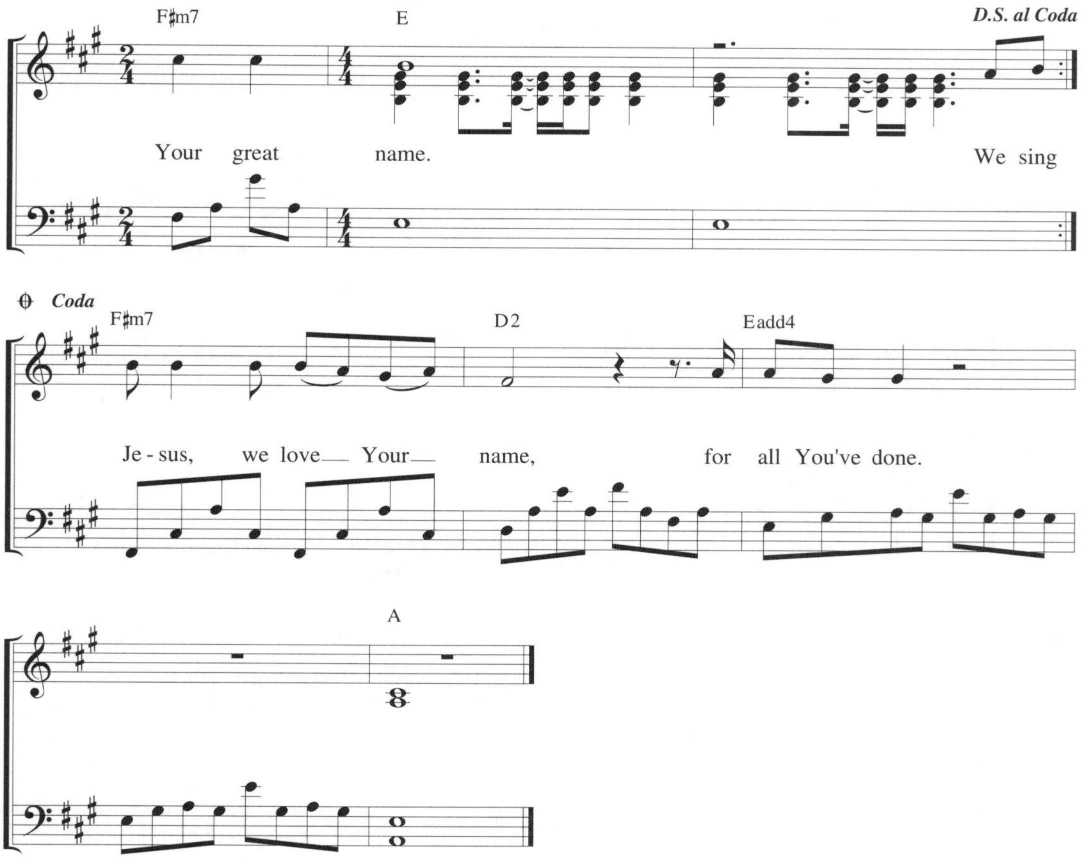

F♯m7 E *D.S. al Coda*

Your great name. We sing

Coda

F♯m7 D2 Eadd4

Je - sus, we love Your name, for all You've done.

A

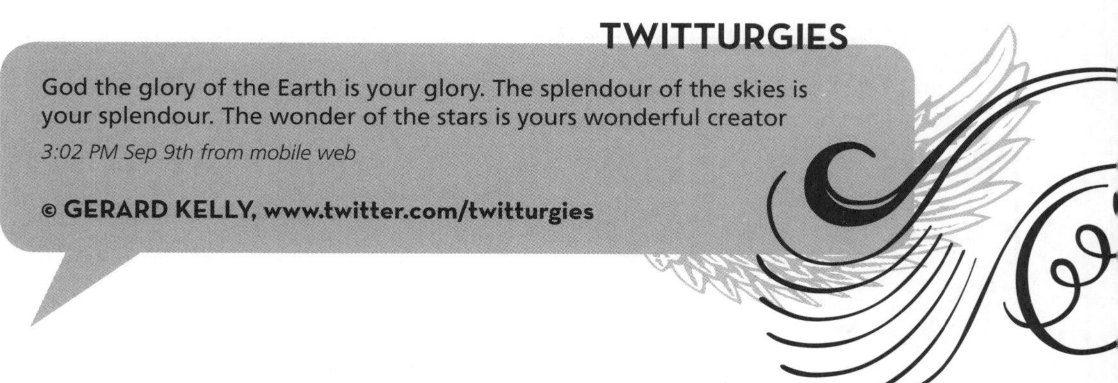

GIVE UNTO THE LORD

(Glorify the King)

Luke Finch

This song is recorded on the Spring Harvest 'Perfect Sacrifice - New Songs 2009' album

Am
Em
D
Chorus
– of glo - ry is po-wer-ful and full of ma - je - sty. – So we glo -
G
D
Em
C
- ri - fy – the King, – glo - ri - fy – the King, – glo -
G
D
Em
1.
C
D.C.
- ri - fy – the King, – glo - ri - fy – the King. –
2.,4.
C
D.S.
3.,5.
C
(Fine)
C2
G
– So we glo - – Glo - ry, glo - ry, glo -
D/F♯
Em
1.
C
2.
C
D.S.
- ry, glo - ry, ev - 'ry-one in his tem - ple cries – out. Glo - - ple cries – out. Glo -

25. GOD WHOSE VOICE CALLED WORLDS

(Through Jesus' eyes)

Graham Kendrick
Arr. Henry George

Chorus
G Bm A Bm7 A G D
in this dark hour.
sees har - vest now.
Your Church, Your Bride.
to meet this hour.
God All - see - ing, God All - Know - ing
G D Em A Bm7 F♯ G D
heal our vi - sion, make us wise; cleanse, re - new, re - vive, in - spire us
Bm D G A
1.,-3.
Bm Bm7/A G A D
to see the world through Je - sus' eyes, through Je - sus' eyes.
Bm G D
4.
Bm7 G A
eyes,
Bm A G D G D Em A
God All - see - ing, God All - Know - ing heal our vi - sion, make us wise;

CALLING OUT TO THE GOD OF JUSTICE

To the cries of the poor;
Loving God, open your heart.

To the cries of the landless;
Loving God, open your heart.

To the cries of those enslaved by people and systems;
Loving God, open your heart.

And when you hear their cries, bring your love and justice to bear.

To the cries of the poor;
Loving God, open our hearts.

To the cries of the landless;
Loving God, open our hearts.

To the cries of those enslaved by people and systems;
Loving God, open our hearts.

And when we hear their cries,
bring us to our knees in prayer
and to our feet in action,
to see your love and justice
come on earth as in heaven.
Amen.

WORSHIP AND JUSTICE CONFESSION

Father, when our worship has been
more about us than about you,
Lord have mercy.

When our songs have ignored the
pain of your broken body on earth,
Christ have mercy.

When our services have been more
of an escape for us, than good
news to the poor,
Lord, have mercy.

When we praise you with our lips,
but deny you with our finances,
Christ, have mercy.

When our instruments are louder
than our cries for justice,
Lord, have mercy.

When we fail to learn from the
sacrificial worship of brothers and
sisters across the world,
Christ, have mercy.

Receiving forgiveness:
May God, who suffered the death
of his only Son for our sake,
forgive us our sins,
cleanse us by the blood of Christ,
and fill us with his Holy Spirit,
to lead lives of worship
that bring his resurrection power to
our broken world,
and inspire us to lead services of
worship
which reflect his heart for justice,
mercy and humility.
In the name of Christ we pray,

Amen.

RESIDE WITH US, LORD

In our prayer and preparation,
through debate and discussion,
by invitation and imagination,
in our worship and witness:
**Let us know your power at
work in our relationships,
our community,
our faith.**

On our fast days and fun days,
by exploration and experience,
through shared suffering and
silence,
by walking and talking:
**Let us know your power at
work in our relationships,
our community,
our faith.**

In our communication and creativity,
through websites and wonderings,
by mailshots and mystery,
through listening and learning:
**Let us know your power at
work in our relationships,
our community,
our faith.**

Through groupwork and generosity,
in negotiation and networking,
by our hospitality and holiness,
by repairing broken walls and
building bridges:
**Let us know your power at
work in our relationships,
our community,
our faith.**

26. GONNA DANCE, DANCE

(Dance)

Tim Hughes

This song is recorded on the Spring Harvest 'Journey - Live Worship 2009' album

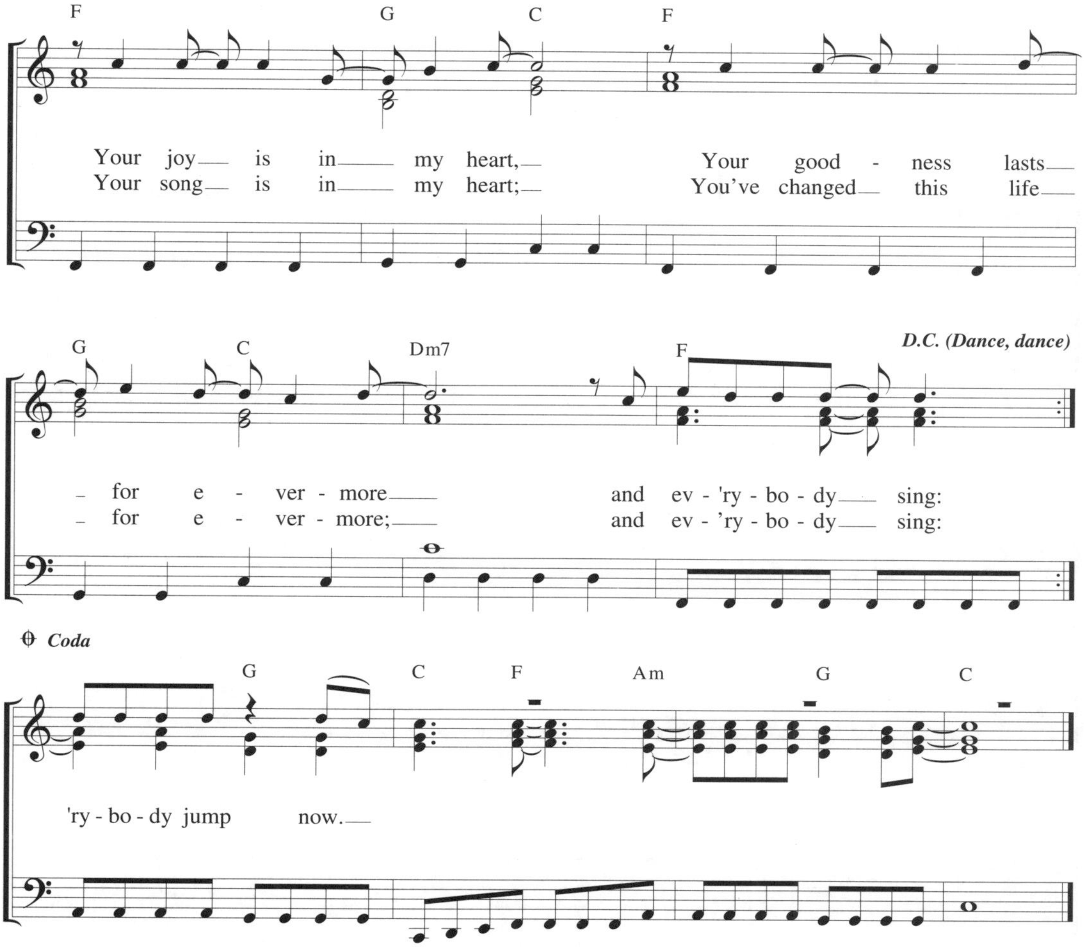

F G C F

Your joy is in my heart, Your good - ness lasts
Your song is in my heart; You've changed this life

G C Dm7 F *D.C. (Dance, dance)*

for e - ver - more and ev - 'ry - bo - dy sing:
for e - ver - more; and ev - 'ry - bo - dy sing:

Coda

G C F Am G C

'ry - bo - dy jump now.

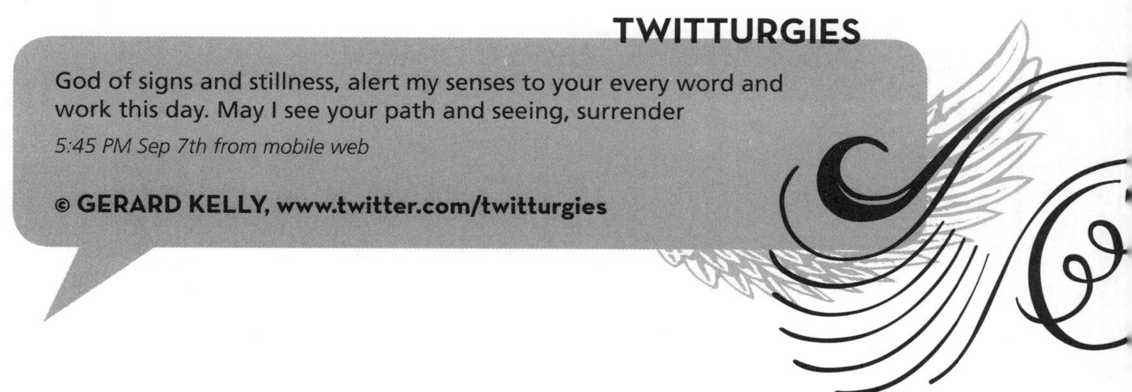

27. HALLELUJAH

Ben Cantelon

This song is recorded on the Spring Harvest 'Journey - Live Worship 2009' album

D(C)
A(G)
1.
E/G♯(D)
it's You we're lift - ing high. Your name be glo - ri - fied.
2.
E/G♯(D)
F♯m(Em)
D(C)
A(G)
Hal - le - lu - jah, hal - le - lu - jah.
E/G♯(D)
F♯m(Em)
D(C)
1.
A(G)
You are wor - thy of our praise.
E/G♯(D)
2.
A(G)
Hal - le - praise.

28. HAVE YOU HEARD

Fadd4(D) B♭(G) E♭maj7(C) Gm(Em)
the love that God has shown; oh, the joy
the love that God has shown; oh, the joy
F/A(D) E♭/B♭ (C) B♭(G) Last time to Coda E♭/G (C)
of for - give - ness. Come, oh come,
of for - give - ness. Sing, oh sing,
F/A(D) B♭(G) E♭maj7(C)
let us kneel be - fore the cross; this is
of the God who came to us: this is
F(D) 1. E♭maj7(C) Gm(Em) E♭(C)
love, this is love.
F(D) Gm(Em) E♭(C) B♭(G) F(D)

Gm(Em) E♭(C) F(D) Gm(Em) E♭(C) B♭(G) F(D)
D.C. (v.3)
2.
D.C. (v.4)
E♭maj7(C) F(D) B♭(G) B♭/A(G)
love. this is love, this is love.
3.
D.S. (last chorus) al Coda
Coda
B♭(G) E♭(C) D7(B)
love. Sing, oh sing, of the
Gm(Em) C/E(A) Cm/E♭(Am) F(D)
God who came to us: This is love,
E♭(C) (repeat 4 times) B♭(G)
this is love. This is love.

HE IS JEALOUS FOR ME

29.

(See His love)

Justin Byrne

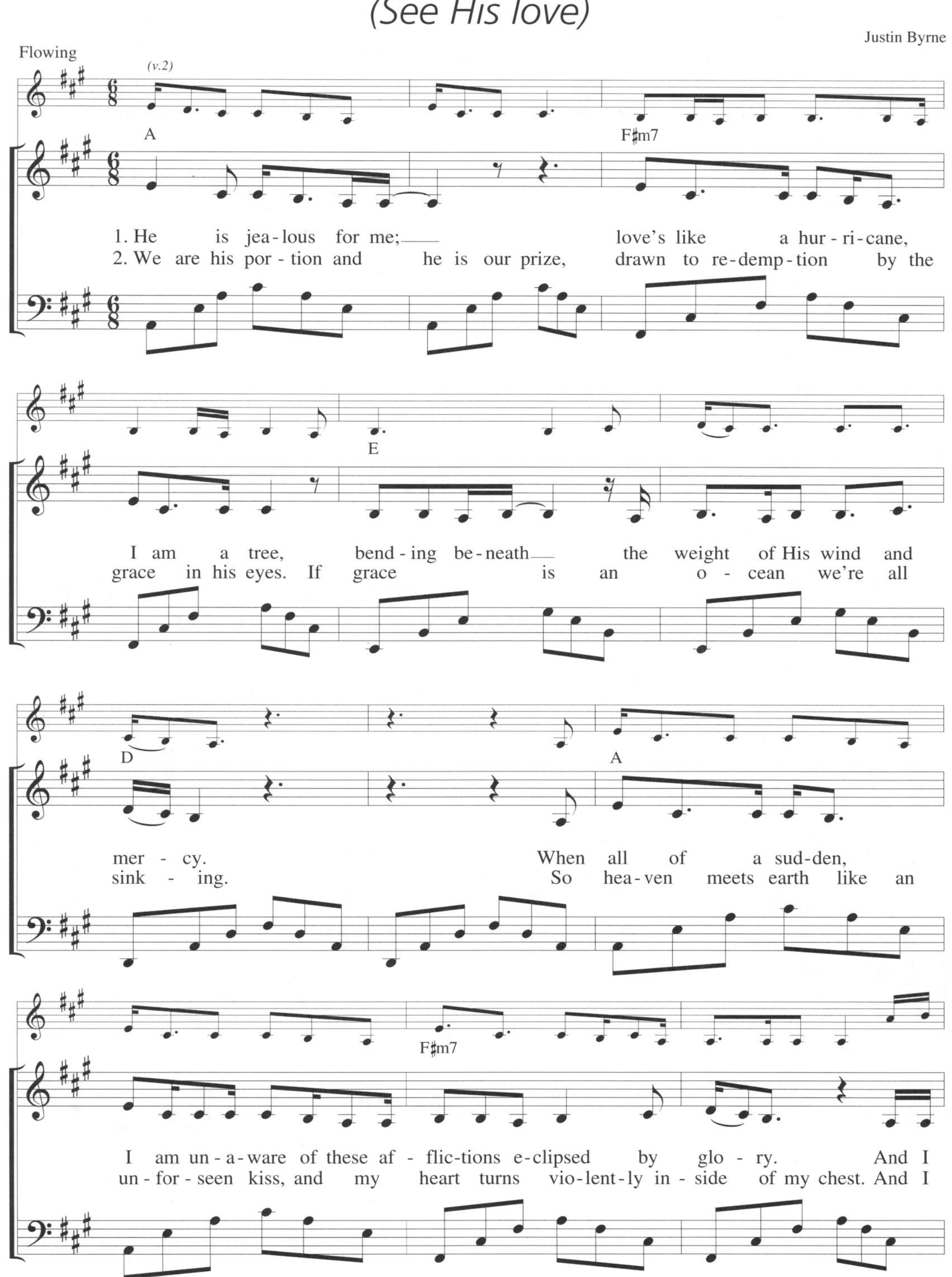

This song is recorded on the Spring Harvest 'Glory - New Songs 2010' album

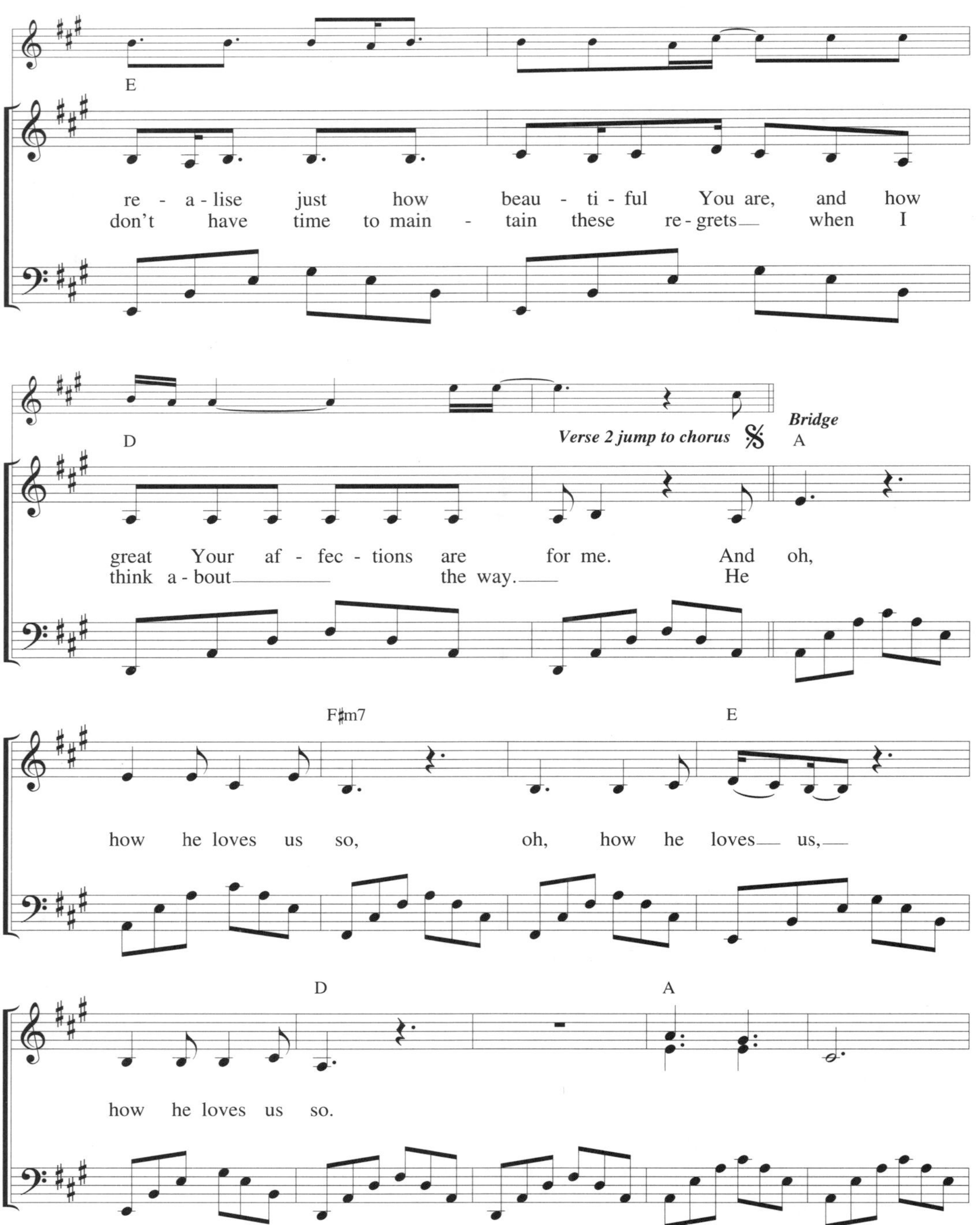
E
re - a - lise just how beau - ti - ful You are, and how
don't have time to main - tain these re - grets when I
D
Verse 2 jump to chorus
Bridge
A
great Your af - fec - tions are for me. And oh,
think a - bout the way. He
F♯m7
E
how he loves us so, oh, how he loves us,
D
A
how he loves us so.

F♯m7
E
1.
D2
D.C. (v.1)
2.
D2
Chorus
A
Yeah, he loves us,
F♯m7
E
oh, how he loves us, oh, how he loves us, oh, how he
1.,3.
2.
D.C. (v.2)
Last time
D
A
loves. Yeah, he

30. HERE INSIDE YOUR PRESENCE

(Burning ones)

Chris Quilala
& Jeffrey Kunde

This song is recorded on the Spring Harvest 'Glory - New Songs 2010' album

2.,3.
Chorus
Bm
And we cry ho - ly,
F♯m7
G
ho - ly are You.
And we cry
v.2 Our hearts are
F♯m7
Bm
ho - ly, ho - ly are You.
burn - ing, burn - ing for You.
D.C. (v.2)
Mid section
G
A
2. Your
We are Your burn - ing ones,
Bm
E
G
we are con - sumed by You,
we set our lives a - part,

LIVING THE DIFFERENCE

Bonded like a molecule, may we nurture our relationships.
Growing like a tree, may we be rooted in our community.
Drawn like a magnet, may others be attracted to the joy of our faith.

HOPE IS HERE

(Jesus saves)

31.

Capo 4(G)

Tim Hughes
& Nick Herbert

Moderately

This song is recorded on the Spring Harvest 'Glory - New Songs 2010' album

E/B(C) B(G) Chorus E(C)
Je - sus saves.
Je - sus saves.
1. Hope is here,
2. Free at last
what a joy-
F♯(D) E(C) G♯m(Em) F♯/A♯(D/F♯)
- ful noise we'll make, as we join in hea - ven's song
F♯(D) G♯m(Em) E(C)
to let all the world know that Je - sus saves.
B(G) F♯(D) G♯m(Em)
Raise a shout to let all the world know that
Last time to Coda
1. D.S.
3. D.S.S. al Coda
E(C) B(G) B(G)
Je - sus saves. 2. Free at last Sing it out

TWITTURGIES

God is the road I take; God the city it leads to. God waves me off; God waits to welcome me. God is my journey: God my goal

8:57 PM Aug 9th from web

32. HOLY, HOLY IS THE LORD GOD ALMIGHTY

Eb(C)
F(D)
1.
Bbsus4(G)
Bb(G)
Cm7(Am)
filled with Your glo - ry.
filled with Your glo -
Bb(G)
Cm7(Am)
Bb(G)
D.C.
2.
Bbsus4(G)
Bb(G)
D.S. (Ch.2)
ry. Let the
3.
Gm7(Em) F2(D)
Ebmaj7(C)
F(D)
Gm7(Em) F2(D) Cm7(Am) F(D)
ry. Your glo - ry, Your glo -
Bbsus4(G)
Bb(G)
ry.

33. HOW GREAT IS YOUR LOVE

(All glory)

E♭(C)
Fsus4(D)
B♭2/D(G)
1.
E♭6⁹(C)
will pro-claim: You are migh - ty, You are migh - ty.
D.C. (v.2)
2.
E♭6⁹(C)
D.S.
3.,4.
E♭(D)
F(D)
B♭/D(G)
Last time to Coda
- ty. - ty. He is migh - ty, he is migh-
E♭(D)
Mid section
F(D)
B♭/D(G)
E♭(C)
- ty. Lift him high - er, he is migh - ty; lift him high-
F(D)
B♭/D(G)
1.
E♭2(C)
2.
E♭2(C)
D.S. al Coda
- er, he is God. Lift him high
Coda
E♭maj7(C)
- ty.

34. I AM AN INSTRUMENT OF THE LIVING GOD
(Sweet, sweet sound)

Capo 3(D)
Steadily, building

Ed Cash
& Sarah Reeves

This song is recorded on the Spring Harvest 'Glory - New Songs 2010' album

Dm(Bm)
1.
D.C. (v.1)
B♭2(G)
sweet, sweet sound, let it be a sweet, sweet sound. 1. I am an
2.,Last time
(Fine)
D.C. (v.2)
3.,4.
(2nd time D.S al Fine)
B♭2(G)
B♭2(G)
sweet, sweet sound. 2. Through all the sweet, sweet sound. (Let)
Mid section
Gm(Em)
Gm/F(Em)
C/E(A)
ev - 'ry - thing that has breath praise the Lord, praise the
C(A)
Gm(Em)
Gm/F(Em)
Lord. And all cre - a - tion will sing hal - le - lu-
E♭(C)
C/E(A)
D.S.
- jah.

35.

I AM CHOSEN

(Holding nothing back)

Tim Hughes
& Martin Smith

B(G)
Bridge
E(C)
G♯m(Em)
And no - thing's gon - na hold me
F♯(D)
back, no - thing's gon - na hold me back,
no - thing's gon - na hold me back.
Chorus
My chains fell off, my heart was free,
A - maz - ing love, how can it be?
I'm a - live to live for You, I'm - a - live
You gave ev - 'ry-thing for me, You gave ev -

Last time to Coda
1.,4.
2.
F♯(D)
Emaj7(C)
to live for You.
'ry-thing for me,
ev - 'ry - thing.
D.C. (v.2)
3.
Mid section
E(C)
And I'm free to live, free
F♯(D)
G♯m(Em)
1.
to give, free to be, I'm free to love You. Free
2.
E(C)
F♯(D)
G♯m(Em)
to love You. Free to live, free to give, free to be, I'm free
E(C)
D.S.
to love You, Lord.

GOD OF GRACE AND LOVE

God of grace and love, forgive us.
We turn from our sins, and our lack of trust,
God of grace and love, forgive us.
We turn from our sins, and our holding back,
God of grace and love, forgive us.
We turn from our sins, and seek your healing,
God of grace and love, forgive us.

36. I SEE YOUR FACE

(You're beautiful)

Phil Wickham

Esus4
E
A
D
You're beau - ti - ful.
F♯m7
E
4th time jump to v.4
5th time to Coda
A
Verse
2. I see Your pow - er in the
3. I see You there hang - ing
D
F♯m7
Esus4
E
moon - lit night, where pla - nets are in mo - tion and ga - la - xies are bright.
on a tree, You bled and then You died and then You rose a - gain for me.
A
D
We are a - mazed in the light of the stars; it's
Now You are sit - ting on Your hea - ven - ly throne;
F♯m7
(small notes v.2)
Esus4
E
D.S.
all pro - claim - ing who You are:
soon we will be com - ing home:
You're beau - ti - ful.
You're beau - ti - ful.

A
D
F♯m7
4. When we ar-rive at e-ter-ni-ty's shore, where death is just a me-mo-ry and
Esus4
E
A
D
tears are no more, we'll en-ter in as the wed-ding bells ring; Your
F♯m7
Esus4
E
D.S. al Coda
bride will come to-ge-ther and we'll sing: You're beau-ti-ful.
Coda
Tag
A
D
F♯m7
I see Your face, You're beau-ti-ful, You're beau-ti-ful, You're
Esus4
E
A
D
beau-ti-ful. I see Your face, You're beau-ti-ful, You're

A PRAYER FOR DIRECTION

When the global future seems uncertain, changeable and overwhelming,
Help us to find our direction and hope
In you, the One True God and Creator.
When society seems broken, untrustworthy and closed,
Help us to invest in our relationships
With one another and the wider community.
When patterns of thinking seem perplexing, confusing and obscure,
Help us to return to the eternal vision
That is linked to the arrival of your Kingdom.
Lord, help us to value your creation, inspire us as a nation and
Transform us to be better people.
Come and heal our land. Amen

37.

I STAND AMAZED

(Jesus died my soul to save)

Matt Bowell

Last time to Coda
F C/E F Gsus4 G
1.
C F/G
D.C. (v.2)
lou - der, the re - frain: Je - sus died my soul to save.
2. A - tone - ment
3.
C
D.S.
2.
C
Mid section
G Am
save. What depth of save.
Oh, such plea - sure, oh, such
Fmaj7 G Am Fmaj7 G Am
pain; the Fa - ther's wrath and fu - ry laid, on Christ whom saints and an - gels
Fmaj7 Dm7 C/E F2
D.C. (v.3)
praise: Je - sus died my soul to save.
3. Come ye
Coda
G C G/B Am F G C
soul to save.

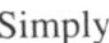

38. I WILL EXALT YOU

Brooke Ligertwood

Simply

Verse

D D/F♯ G2 D D/F♯ G2

1. I will ex - alt You, I will ex - alt You,
with me, be-cause You're with me,

D D/F♯ G2 A *1.,3.,6.* D *(Fine)*

I will ex - alt You, You are my God.
be-cause You're with me, I will not fear.

D D/F♯ *5.* *D.C. al fine* D D/F♯ *2.,4.* D *Chorus*

1. I will ex - fear. 1. I will ex - God. My hid -
2. Be - cause You're fear.

𝄋 A Em7 A/C♯

- ing place, my safe re - fuge, my trea - sure, Lord, You are.

D
A
Em7
D
G
Bm
My Friend and King, a-noin-ted One, most ho-ly.
2.,3.
D.S.
1.,4.
A
A/C♯
D
D/F♯
G2
My hid-
A/C♯ D
D/F♯
G2
A/C♯ D
D/F♯
G2
1.
2.,3.
1° D.C.(v.2 - repeated)
2° D.C.(v.1) al fine
A
D
A/C♯ D
D/F♯
D/F♯
2. Be-cause You're
1. I will ex-

39. I WILL CAST MY CARES

Steadily

Cathy Burton

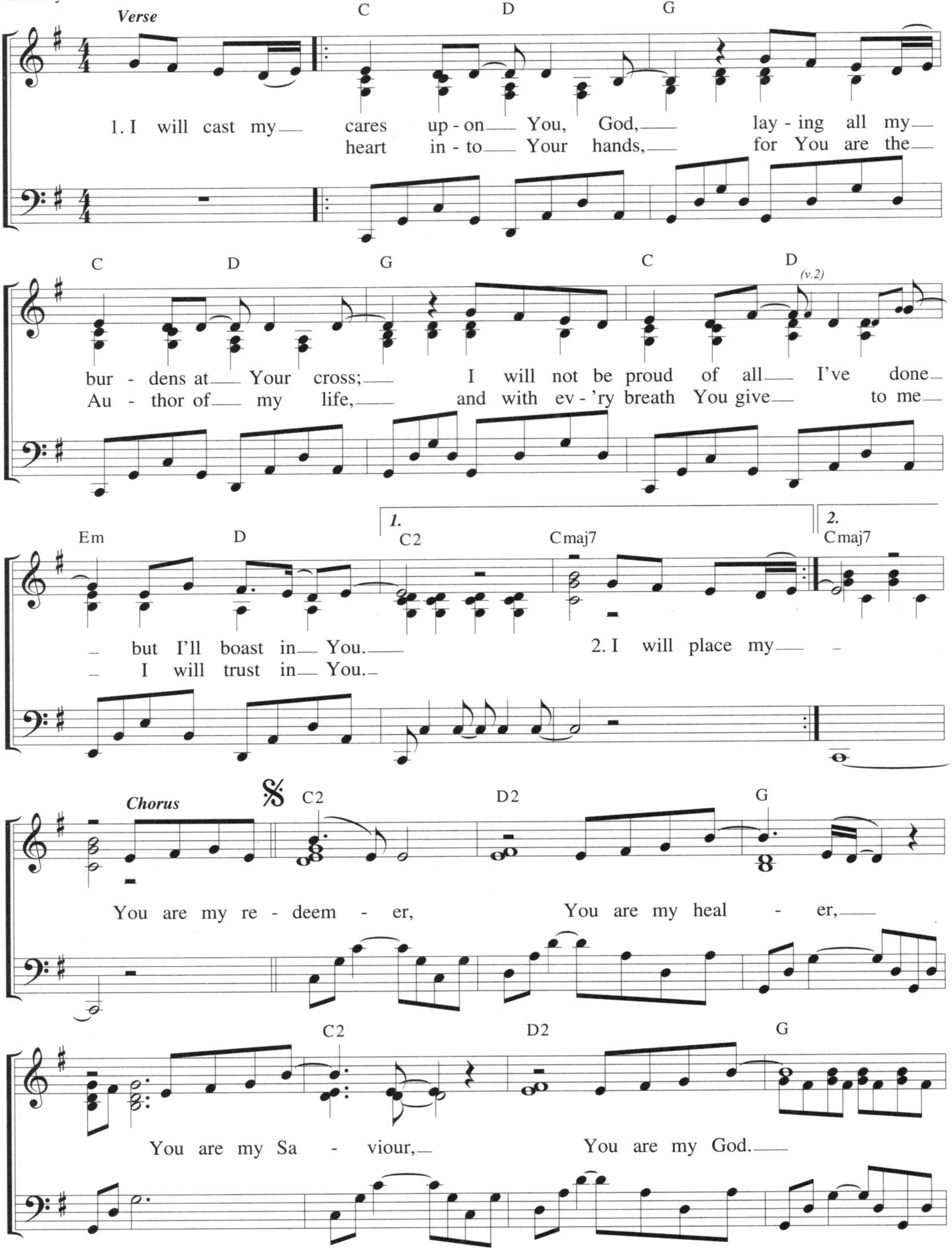

Verse

1. I will cast my cares upon You, God, laying all my burdens at Your cross; I will not be proud of all I've done but I'll boast in You.

2. I will place my heart into Your hands, for You are the Author of my life, and with ev'ry breath You give to me I will trust in You.

Chorus

You are my redeemer,
You are my healer,
You are my Saviour,
You are my God.

C2
D2
You are my De - fen - der,
the source of ev - 'ry
Em
D/F♯
C2
D2
hour.
You are my rea - son,
You are my God.
1.,3.
(Fine)
D.C.(v.2)
Em
G
C
Em
G
Cmaj7
2. I will place my
2.
Gsus4
G
Gsus4
G
Mid section
Am7
Je - sus, my Re - deem -
C2
G
D
Dsus4
D
er, ran - somed now I stand.

Am7 C2 G

Je - sus, my Re - deem - er, You have won me back.

D Am7 C

My Re - deem - er, my Sa - viour, my Com -

Em D *D.S. al fine*

- for - ter and Re - scu - er. You are my Re -

TWITTURGIES

Faith falters; strength fails; hopes fade; passions fall. Love stands; love renews; love revives; love lifts. And God is love

10:14 PM Aug 2nd from web

I WILL NOT BOAST OF ANYTHING

(Jesus is alive today)

Stuart Barbour

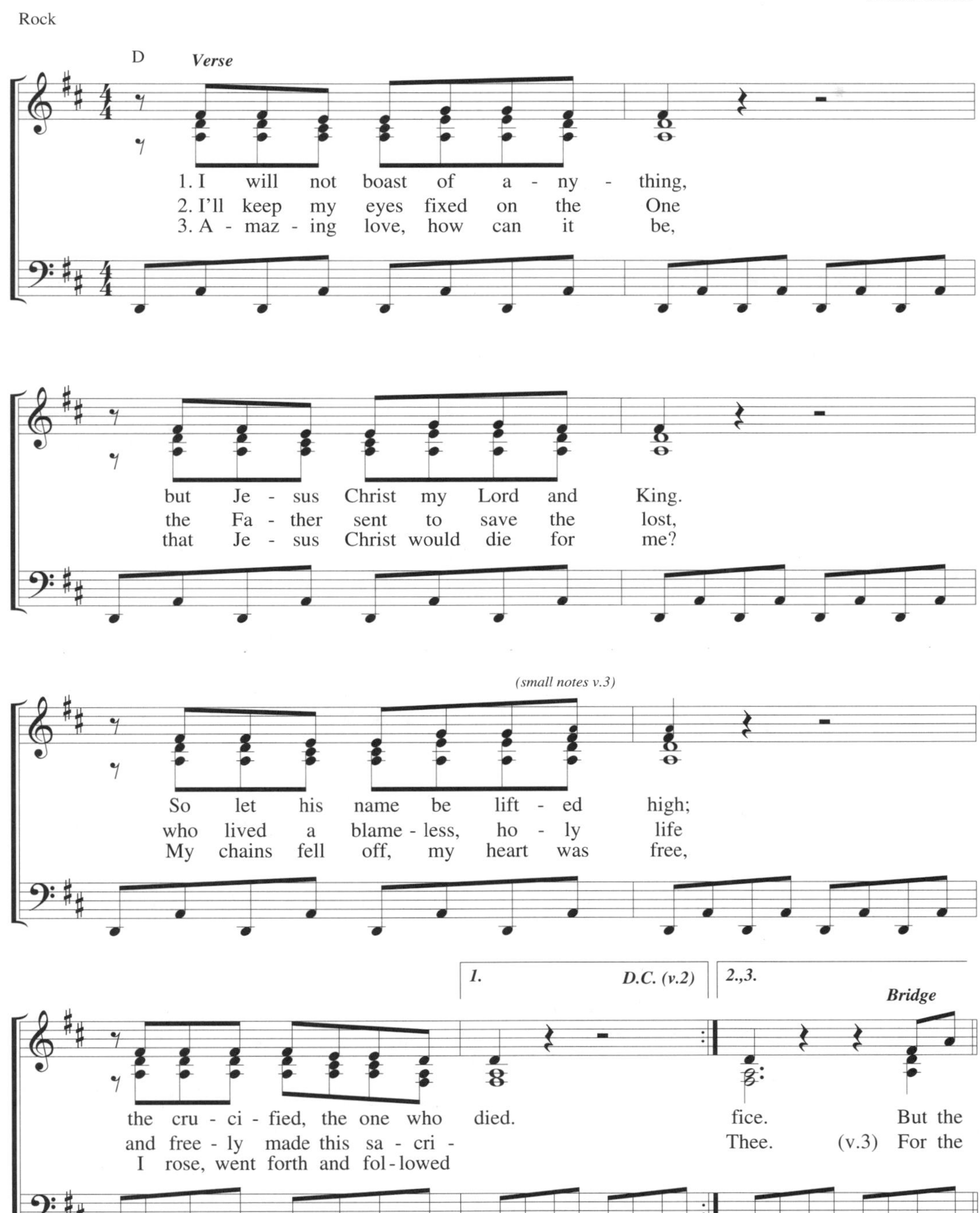

This song is recorded on the Spring Harvest 'Glory - New Songs 2010' album

G D Bm A
grave could not hold him, and the earth be-gan to shake; on the
G D Bm A
third day he a-rose, the Sa-viour of the world.
Chorus
D G A
Je - sus is a-live to - day; the King of love, the
G D G
ri-sen Son. Je - sus is a-live to - day,
Last time to Coda
1.
A G D
ce-le - brate the ho-ly One.

D.C. (v.3)
2.
D.S.
Coda
G
G
ho - ly One.
ho - ly One.
D
Ce - le - brate.
1.
2.
Ce - le - brate. Ce - le - brate.

41. I'LL REMEMBER YOU

(Remember)

Capo 2(D)

Tim Hughes
& Rachel Hughes

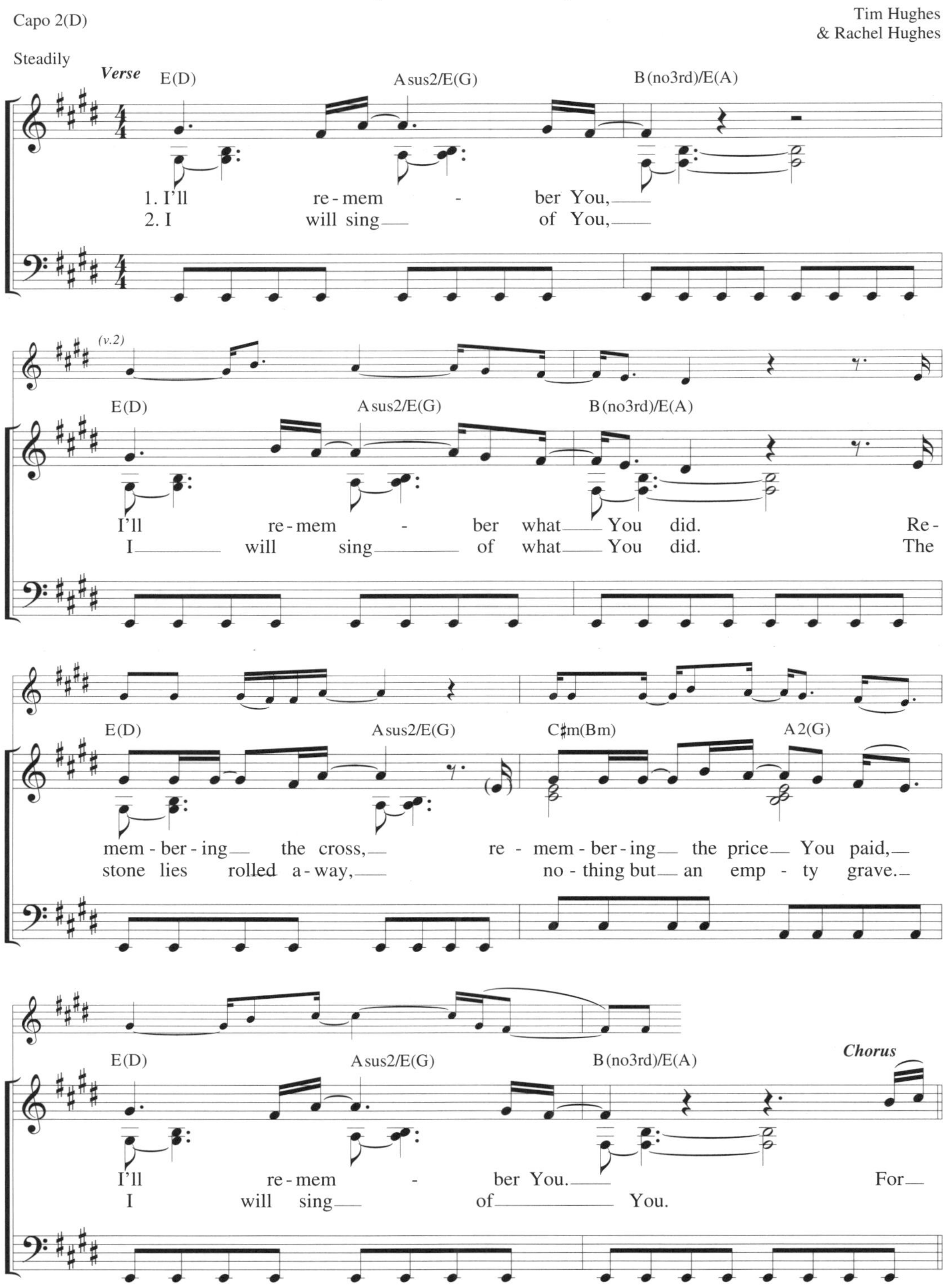

Amaj7(G)
Bsus4(A)
E/G♯(D)
Amaj7(G)
no one's e-ver loved me quite like You do, no one's e-ver loved me
Bsus4(A)
C♯m(Bm)
Amaj7(G)
Bsus4(A)
E/G♯(D)
quite like You; Je-sus, for Your glo-ry, I will tell the sto-ry of the
Last time to Coda
1.
D.C.(v.2)
2.
Mid section
Asus2(G)
Asus2(G)
cross. 2. And Hal-le-
A(G)
B(A)
C♯m(Bm)
lu-jah, hal-le-lu-jah, hal-le-lu-jah for the cross.
B(A)
A(G)
B(A)
Hal-le-lu-jah, hal-le-lu-jah, hal-le-

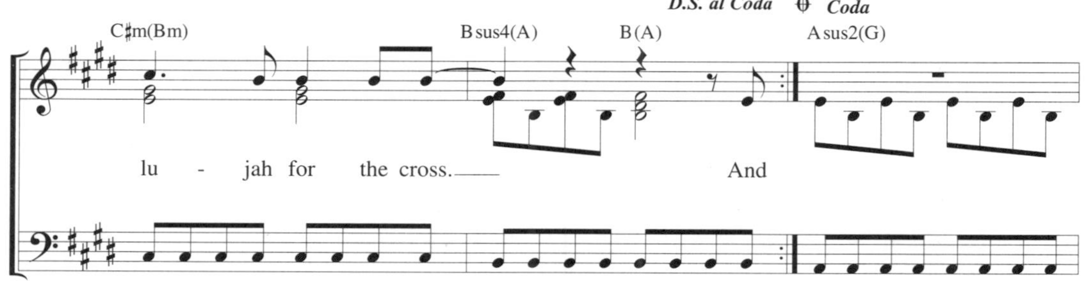

TWITTURGIES

When circumstances are hard and heavy, God give me a weightlifter's strength. When challenges are steep and high, make me a mountain-climber

7:12 AM Jul 17th from mobile web

SING TO THE LORD A NEW SONG
DJ-LED WORSHIP

Steve Leach

40 years ago guitars took over from organs in many churches, reflecting what was going on in contemporary culture. A generation emerged who found this musical expression of their love for God more meaningful.

The reality is that these days, when young people go for a night out or to a party it's far more likely they'll go to see a DJ than a band. When they listen to radio almost all the music is produced electronically. As I write, for example, the UK top 40 has only six tracks by bands but 34 tracks by DJs or producers.

Does the worship in our churches reflect this? And can the soulless, repetitive, and overloud racket which many hear when they hear Dance music really be worshipful? (Ring any bells from descriptions of band-based worship music from 40 years ago?)

Forever God has loved his people delighting themselves in his creation and acknowledging him; what an incredibly exciting opportunity we have, therefore, living in a time when so many new forms of musical and multi-media production are available to us. It's a bit like an artist, who has only ever drawn with a pencil suddenly being given a coloured painting set: there's a whole new dimension to her art. Nowadays she has 16 million colours to choose from via her digital camera and even the ability to create animation on her iMac. Some will say it's not real art, but God sees her heart, and loves the time and effort she's spending on making something as beautiful as she can, with every available tool, for his glory.

DJ-led worship is not better than guitar and band-led worship, any more than guitars are better than the organ, but it does need promoting because of a significant deficit on the current landscape. But I guess the big question is 'How?' This might seem like a whole new language to learn. Let's consider a few practical suggestions.

Firstly, the whole environment may need rethinking. Traditional church buildings, their seating, lighting and acoustics are designed with organ and choir in mind, just as newer churches in industrial estate warehouses are usually designed for a band. But imagine a space with no seats, so people feel free to move around. Think nice and dark so people aren't worried about how silly their dancing looks. (We might not all have the boldness of David in 2 Sam 6:14!) Think really loud so people can call out to God at the top of their voices. Rather than standing in rows, singing the same thing at the same time together, it's about creating an environment where we are comfortable and encouraged to express to God our inmost yearnings; either of adoration and praise, or of intercessory fervency for a kingdom to come here on earth as it is in heaven.

In practice, this whole experience isn't really something that the standard Sunday morning service can reasonably accommodate, even for a token five minutes, but a designated evening of this nature once in a while could be an incredibly significant time of encounter with God for some of your younger (at heart) people.

Maybe a specific track could be used as part of a regular service, more meditatively, with no expectations that people are going to jump up and dance. Leave people sat, dim the lights, maybe project some visuals, and watch for the response.

Finally be aware that when you're trialling this with your lot, they're most likely to be those who are pretty happy with the worship as it is. DJ-led worship is designed to resonate more with the masses in our country who won't come anywhere near our worship the way it is now, so if your congregation doesn't like it, that's ok, it's kind of... not for them. This is all a massive challenge for us, but also an incredible opportunity. Most of all, most of all, it's because our God deserves it.

Steve Leach

42. I'M CASTING MY CARES ASIDE
(Today is the day)

Lincoln Brewster
& Paul Baloche

This song is recorded on the Spring Harvest 'Glory - New Songs 2010' album

Em7
G
Chorus
D
it's good. To-day is the day You have made,
A/C♯
Bm7
G 2
I will re-joice and be glad in it. To-day is the day
D
A/C♯
Bm7
You have made, I will re-joice and be glad in it.
G 2
Em7
Last time to Coda
D/F♯
And I won't wor - ry a-bout to - mor - row; I'm
G
A
D
Bm7
trust-ing in what You say. To-day is the day,

Asus4
G2
1.
D
Bm7
Asus4
G2
D.C. (v.2)
to-day is the day.
2. I'm put-ting my fears
2.
D
Bm7
Asus4
G2
Mid section
D2
I will stand up-on
Your truth.
(I will stand up-on Your truth.)
And all
1.
my days I'll live for You.
(All my days I'll live
(opt. 8va on rpt.)
2.
Em
C
G
D.S.
for You.)
And I my days I'll live.)
To-day is the day

Coda
D/F♯
G
A
– to - mor - row. I'm giv - ing You my fears and sor - rows. Where
Em
D/F♯
G
– You lead me, I will fol - low; I'm trust-ing in what You say:
A
D
Bm7
Asus4
G2
– to-day is the day.
To-day is the day.
D
Bm7
Asus4
G2
D
Bm7
To-day is the day.
Asus4
G2
D
Bm7
Asus4
G2
D2
To-day is the day.
To-day is the day!

43. I'M NOT BACKING DOWN

(Give us Your courage)

Tim Hughes

This song is recorded on the Spring Harvest 'Journey - Live Worship 2009' album

Chorus
(small notes 2nd x)
G
To the ends of the earth we will go, to the ends
of Your word we will stand, for the truth
D
(small notes 2nd x)
Am
of the earth we will go; fill us with pow - er,
of Your word we will stand; give us Your cou - rage,
Last time to Coda
C
1.,3.,5.
2.
D.C.(v.2)
fill us with pow - er. For the truth
give us Your cou - rage.
4.
Mid section
D
C
G/B
Would You breathe on us, would You breathe on
Am7
D
C
G/B
us, would You breathe on us, would You breathe on

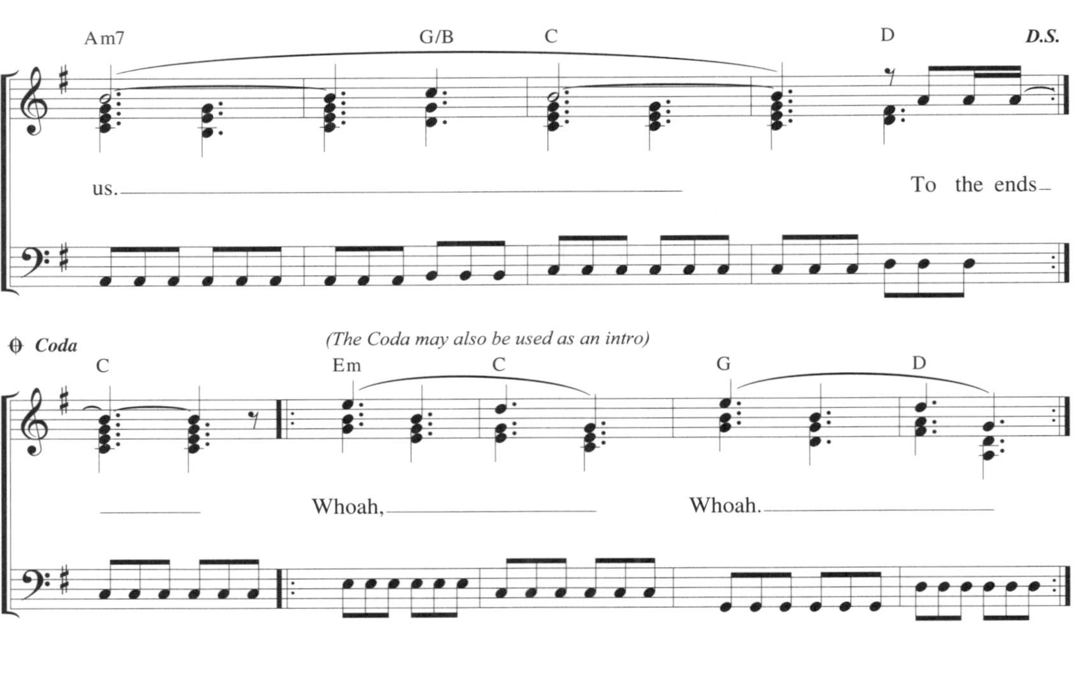

COME NOW TO WORSHIP THE ONE GOD

Come now to worship the One God:
God of all time, God of all creation, God of all people.
Come now to worship the One God:
God of our time, God of our creation, God of our needs.
Come now to worship the One God.

IN THE BEGINNING

(Breath of God)

44.

Vicky Beeching

Capo 3(G)
With increasing intensity

(v.2)

Verse

Gm(Em) E♭(C) B♭(G) F/A(D)

1. In the be - ginn - ing was dark - ness and no - thing, Your
2. Bones in a val - ley were changed in - to an ar - my,

(v.2)

Gm(Em) E♭(C) F(D)

Spi - rit was mo - ving o - ver the deep.
raised by your Spi - rit's po - wer - ful touch.

Gm(Em) E♭(C) B♭(G) F/A(D)

You spoke a whis - per and cre - a - tion ex - ist - ed,
Here in your pre - sence, I'm need - ing your re - fresh - ing;

Gm(Em) E♭(C) *Bridge*

birthed by the migh - ty words that You speak. Just say the
Lord, please re - vive my heart with your love.

This song is recorded on the Spring Harvest 'Journey - Live Worship 2009' and 'Perfect Sacrifice - New Songs 2009' album

Cm7(Am)
B♭2/D(G)
E♭(C)
F/A(D)
Chorus
B♭(G)
word and my wea - ry soul will be re - newed.
Breathe on
F/A(D)
Cm7(Am)
B♭2/D(G)
me O breath of God and fill me with life a -
Fsus4(D)
B♭(G)
F/A(D)
new.
Breathe on me O breath of God and
1.,3. D.C.(v.2)
2.
Mid section
Cm7(Am) B♭2/D(G)
E♭(C)
Fsus4(D)
B♭(G)
(Fine)
F/A(D)
set this heart on fire for You.
Re -
E♭(C)
F(D)
E♭(C)
F(D)
E♭(C)
F(D)
vi - val fire, fall down like the rain. Re - vi - val fire,

E♭(C) F(D) E♭(C) F(D) E♭/G(C)

set my soul a - blaze. Re - vi - val fire, fall down

F/A(D) E♭(C) F(D) E♭/G(C) F/A(D)

like the rain. Re - vi - val fire, set my soul a -

E♭(C) *D.S. al fine*

- blaze.

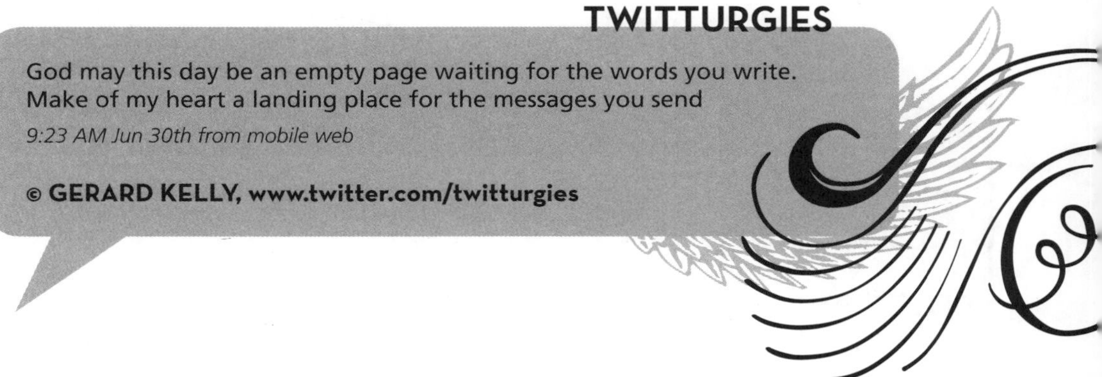

TWITTURGIES

God may this day be an empty page waiting for the words you write. Make of my heart a landing place for the messages you send

9:23 AM Jun 30th from mobile web

45. IT'S FALLING FROM THE CLOUDS

(Cannons)

Phil Wickham

This song is recorded on the Spring Harvest 'Glory - New Songs 2010' album

Chorus
A
D
F♯m
You are ho - ly, great and migh - ty; the moon and the stars de-
E
A
clare who You are. I'm so un - wor - thy, but
D
(small notes 3rd time)
F♯m
Last time to Coda
1.
E
still You love me; for - e - ver my heart will sing of how great You are.
A
D
F♯m
Bm
D.C. (v.2)
3.
E
D.S. al Coda
2.
E
sing of You. And sing of You. All

D
A
E
D
glo-ry, ho-nour, pow-er is Yours, a-men. All glo-ry, ho-nour, pow-er is Yours,
A
E
Bm
a-men. All glo-ry, ho-nour pow-er is Yours
F♯m
Esus4
E
Esus2
E
D.S.
for-e-ver, a-men.
Coda
E
A
D
sing of how great You are.
F♯m
1.
Bm
2.
E
D
A

JESUS YOU ENDURED MY PAIN

46.

(Because of Your love)

Capo 3(D)

Phil Wickham

Steadily, building

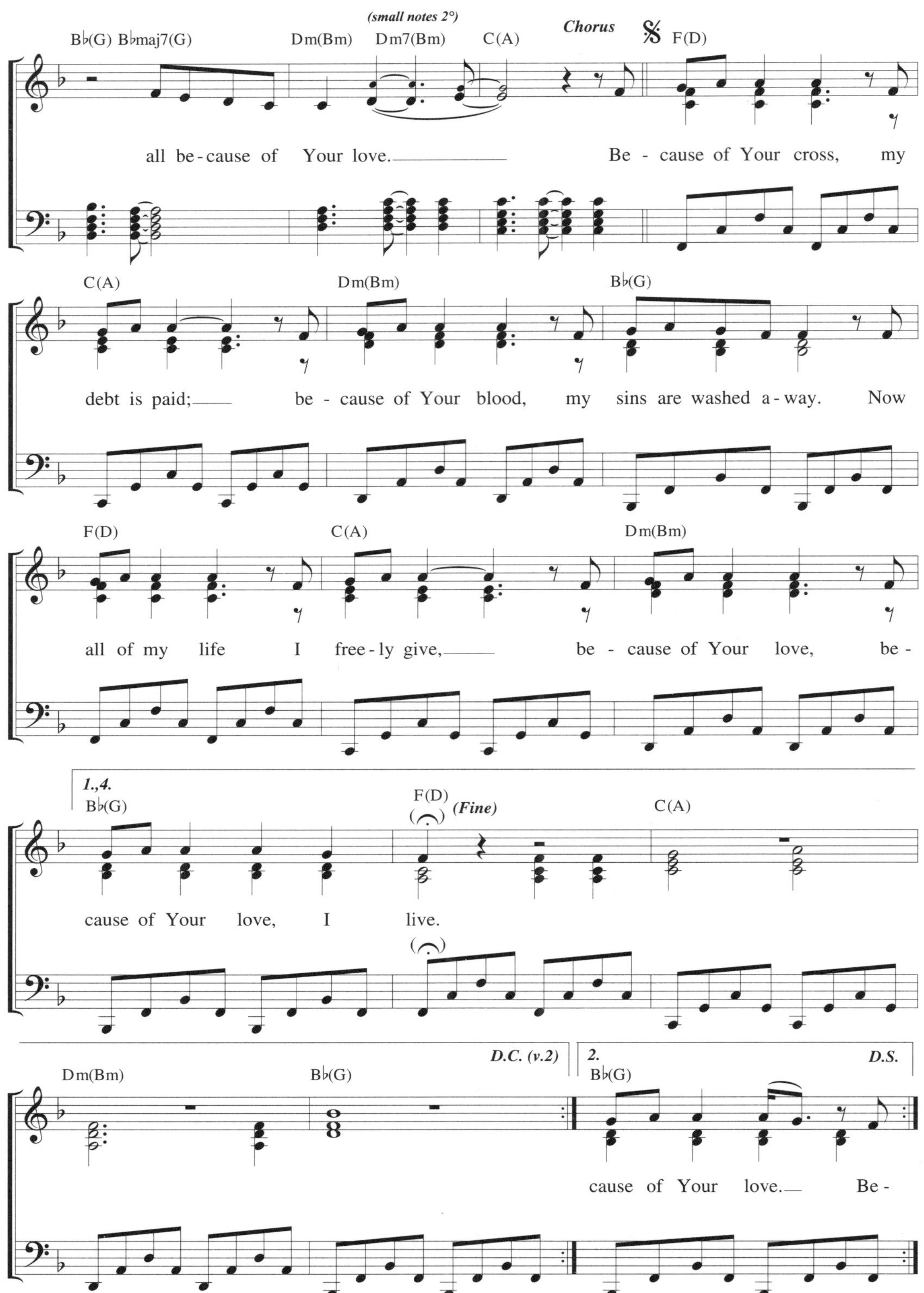
(small notes 2°)
Chorus
B♭(G) B♭maj7(G) Dm(Bm) Dm7(Bm) C(A) F(D)
all be-cause of Your love. Be - cause of Your cross, my
C(A) Dm(Bm) B♭(G)
debt is paid; be - cause of Your blood, my sins are washed a-way. Now
F(D) C(A) Dm(Bm)
all of my life I free-ly give, be - cause of Your love, be -
1.,4.
B♭(G) F(D) (Fine) C(A)
cause of Your love, I live.
D.C. (v.2)
Dm(Bm) B♭(G)
2.
D.S.
B♭(G)
cause of Your love. Be -

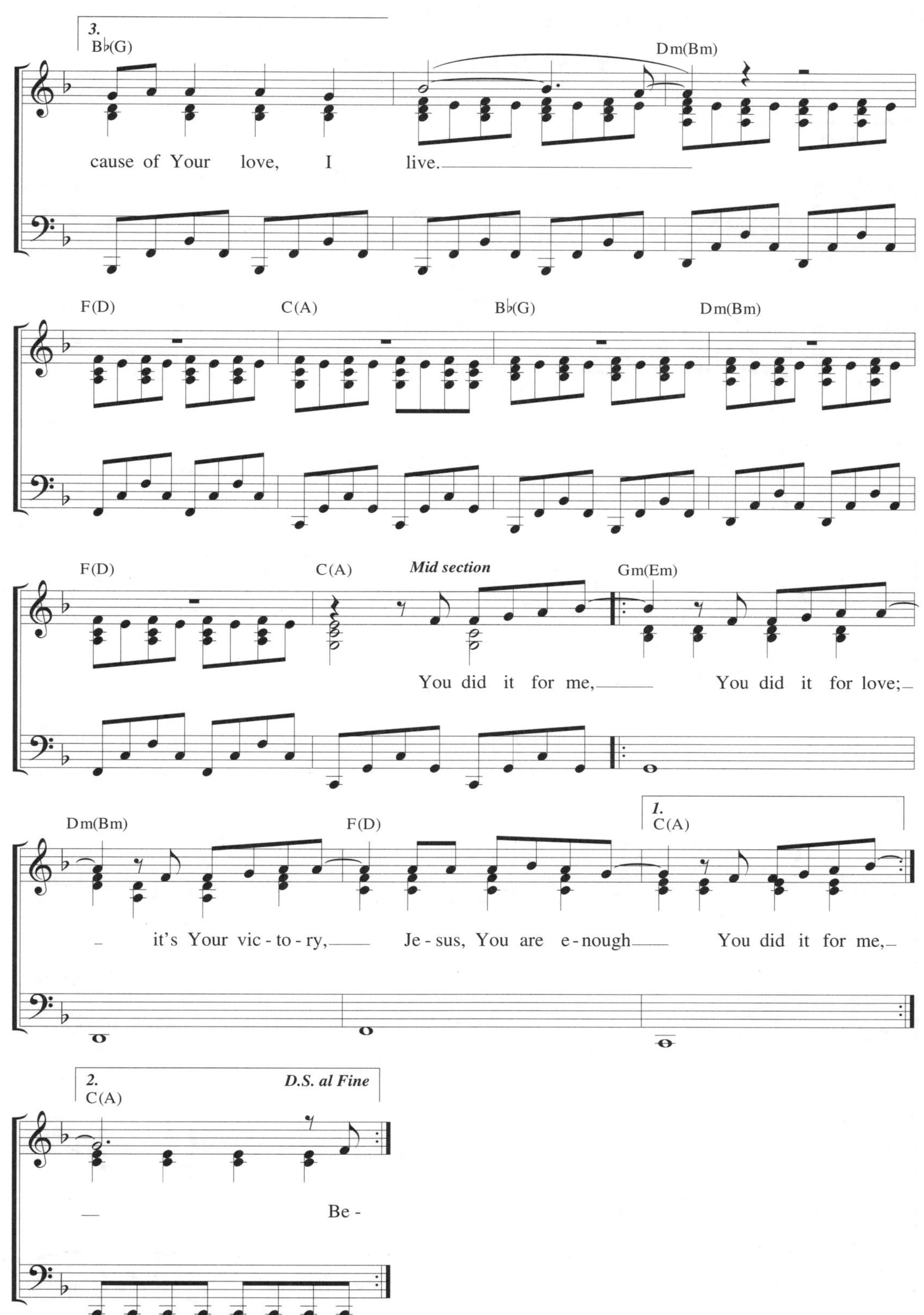
3.
B♭(G)
Dm(Bm)
cause of Your love, I live.
F(D)
C(A)
B♭(G)
Dm(Bm)
F(D)
C(A)
Mid section
Gm(Em)
You did it for me,
You did it for love;
Dm(Bm)
F(D)
1.
C(A)
it's Your vic - to - ry,
Je - sus, You are e - nough
You did it for me,
2.
C(A)
D.S. al Fine
Be -

47. JESUS, BEAUTIFUL SAVIOUR

(Beautiful Saviour)

Henry Seeley

Worshipfully, building

Verse

(opt. 8va on repeat)

A E/G♯ F♯m7 A/E
Je - sus, beau-ti-ful Sa - viour, God of all

D A/C♯ Bm
ma - je - sty, ri - sen King. Lamb of

A E/G♯ F♯m7 A/E
God, ho-ly and right - eous, bles-sed Re -

D A/C♯ Bm
deem - er, Bright Morn-ing Star. All the

E A/C♯ D
hea - vens shout Your praise, all cre -

E
A/C♯
D
D/F♯
E
Chorus
A
a - tion bows to worship You. How won - der
E/G♯
F♯m7
A/E
D
ful, how beau - ti - ful, Name a-bove ev - 'ry
A/C♯
Bm7
D/F♯
E/G♯
A
E/G♯
name, ex - al - ted high. How won - der ful, how
F♯m7
A/E
D
Bm7
beau - ti - ful, Je - sus, Your name, Name a-bove
D
D/F♯
Esus4
E
Asus4
A
Asus4
A (Fine)
ev - 'ry name: Je - sus.

A PRAYER OF DISMISSAL

Lord Jesus, Holy God, you have touched our lives.
We can feel the kindling of your Spirit.
Gently set your fire ablaze within our hearts.
Let us burn for you,
Become beacons of light for you.
And, as we leave this place,
Help us to radiate the warmth of your love. **Amen.**

PLAYING KEYBOARDS IN WORSHIP

Matt Loose

The role of keyboard instruments has changed in churches. Worship has moved from being led by keyboard instruments such as organs and pianos to the worship leader with an acoustic guitar. Partly, I think this is because the guitar is a relatively simple instrument to turn up and play! Before all the guitarists I know start booing me, I better explain! An acoustic guitar takes one person to carry, needs no amplification and works well in a small group, or a large congregation. How often does a guitarist have to ask a friend to carry her acoustic in from the car? At 9am on a Sunday morning, the lot of a keyboard player is not always a happy one! However, keyboards, pianos and organs still have a significant part to play in contemporary worship. (if you have a pipe organ in your church, think about how you can use it in contemporary worship. For ideas about how pipe organs can work in contemporary music listen to Arcade Fire). Here are 10 thoughts that I hope will help you.

Know your instrument.

Make sure you know how your keyboard works! Learn where the sounds are that you like. If you can mix sounds together (play a piano and a pad sound at the same time) make sure you know how to adjust the volume of each. When you are playing, you want to be free to worship, which means you don't want to have to think too hard about which button to press next. Make sure you can play a variety of different sounds, you might want an electric piano sound, an organ sound, a pad sound and others. Experiment and have fun.

You don't have to be the best, but you do have to practice.

No matter how good someone is, they will only have got there by practicing. Practice until you can play the songs without thinking too much. Again, when you are leading worship, you need to be able to model worship. That means you want to be free to worship as you play, not panicking about the next chord!

Keep it simple.

When we lead worship, our job is to serve the congregation and allow them to worship. It isn't our job to impress anyone with our skill and virtuosity. Keep your contribution simple, particularly if you are playing as one part of a band, you will find that simplicity works.

Listen to the other musicians.

If you are playing on your own, then you are making all the music. If you are in a band with four other musicians, then you need to make 1/5th of the total sound. Remember that your left hand (playing the bass notes) is doing the same thing as the bass player. Don't clash with the bass line. Keep the left hand part very simple - or even just play with your right hand only. Your right hand is playing in the same area as the guitar. Therefore listen carefully to the guitarist - make sure you aren't clashing with them.

Watch.

You need to keep your eyes peeled - if you aren't leading the worship, make sure you are watching the person who is. Watch for whatever signals have been arranged for directing the song. Watch the other members of the band, try to maintain eye contact and smile at one another once in a while! Watch the congregation, make sure you know what is happening in the room so that you can play sensitively and serve the congregation as you lead. Even if you yourself are not leading, you need to be playing sensitively.

Listen to other keyboard players.

The best thing you can do is listen to what others have played before. Listen carefully to the keyboard parts of different styles of music. You will discover that most of them are very simple indeed. Don't just restrict yourself to worship music - try to work out what the keyboards are doing in any of your favourite songs.

Learn some theory.

Theory sometimes puts people off, but understanding which chords work well with one another is vital. Ideally you want to learn how to play the same chord in many different ways. This really helps when you are handed a sheet with scribbled guitar chords at 9am on a Sunday morning! There are many basic theory books out there. Find one in a style that you like and give it a go.

Practice.

Finally, I'm going to end by repeating myself. Practice really is the key. Spend 20 to 30 minutes as often as you can playing and practicing. Learn how to worship through your playing when you are alone and that will flow through you when you are playing for a congregation.

Matt Loose

www.trentband.com

Available from all good Christian retailers, iTunes & www.essentialchristian.com

48. JESUS, MY PASSION IN LIFE

(Above all else)

Vicky Beeching

Worshipfully ♩ = 82

This song is recorded on the Spring Harvest 'Journey - Live Worship 2009' album

Chorus
Asus4 A
D/G
D/F♯
Em
A - bove all else,
a - bove all else,
A
G
D/F♯
Em
Last time to Coda
a - bove all else,
give me Your - self.
1.
D
D.C.
2.
D/G
D.S.
A - bove all else,
Coda
D

49. LET THE WORDS OF MY MOUTH

(All for You)

Paul Baloche
& Graham Kendrick

This song is recorded on the Spring Harvest 'Glory - New Songs 2010' album

C♯m(Am) A(F) E(C)
all of me, my strength, my mind. Lord, I want to
F♯m(Dm) C♯m(Am) A(F) C♯m(Am) B(G)
work be-side You and learn of You, Je - sus, till
A(F) C♯m(Am) A(F) D.C.
all I do speaks of You. Let the
Coda
E(C) A/E(F) E(C) A/E(F) E(C)
You, be for You, Lord, all for You, all for You.

50. LIFE COULD TAKE

(Perfect sacrifice)

Lyrics: Nigel Briggs
Music: Trent

This song is recorded on the Spring Harvest 'Perfect Sacrifice - New Songs 2009' album

Last time to Coda
Verse
G
1. I've been cho - sen by Your hand,
chains and took my shame,
2. It's a gift we don't de - serve,
that of - fers more
(2.i)
D/F♯
C
through for - give - ness called Your friend,
on the cross You bore my pain.
a trea - sure we can - not earn,
and a cross that's said it all,
(2.i)
(2.ii)
G
1.
now You're here with me.
Je - sus died for me.
you paid the price.
a per - fect sa - cri - fice.
2.
D.C.
Loosed my
Now a life
So

IF WE REMAIN SILENT

If we remain silent,
who will rise up?

If we close our eyes
and turn our heads,
who will see the injustice?

If we wring our hands
and shuffle our feet,
who will act with mercy?

What if we were called
for such a time as this,
to see through different eyes
and move to a different drum.

Father, give us your strength,
at such a time as this,
to lead distinctive lives,
and see your Kingdom come.

LOOK INSIDE THE MYSTERY

51.

(Glorious)

Paul Baloche
& Brenton Brown

C/G
F2
he a-lone has con-quered the pow-er of the grave.
hope of his re-turn-ing fills the u-ni-verse.
Chorus
F
Glo-ri-ous, my eyes have seen the
ous, he stands a-bove the
C
1.,3.,5.
glo-ry of the Lord. Glo-ri-
ru-lers of the earth.
2.
D.C. (v.2)
4.,6.
Mid section
G
Glo-ri-ous, glo-ri-
Am
F
-ous, Lord, You are glo-ri-

C Cmaj7 Am F

ous.

C Cmaj7 Am F

Oh, ___ You are glo - ri - ous. ___

1. D.S. 2. C

Glo - ri

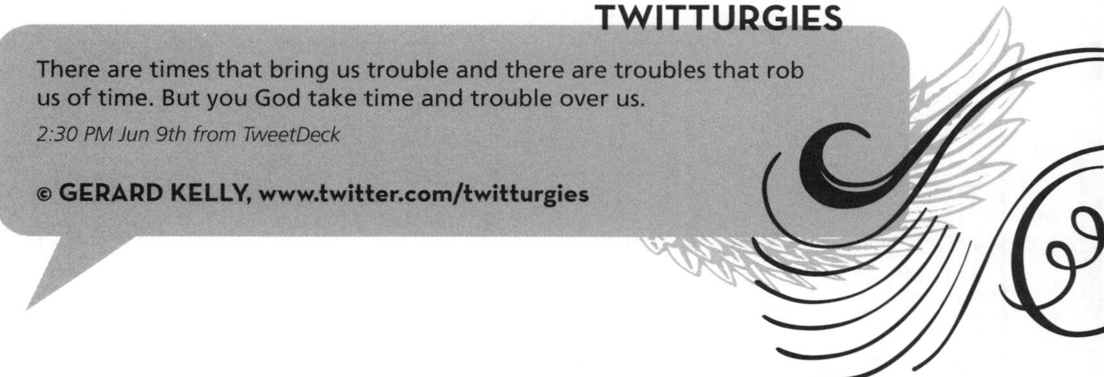

TWITTURGIES

There are times that bring us trouble and there are troubles that rob us of time. But you God take time and trouble over us.

2:30 PM Jun 9th from TweetDeck

52. LORD, MY LIFE IS AN EMPTY CUP

(Just to be with You)

Paul Baloche
& Jason Ingram

D
A/C♯
Bm7
all I need is just to be with You, just to be
G2
D
A/C♯
with You. Here I am, at Your feet, just to be
Last time to Coda
Last chorus D.S. al Coda
1.
D.C. (v.2)
Bm7
G2
(Small notes last°)
with You, just to be with You. (All I want) 2. I have
2.
Mid section
G
D
Bm7
Asus4
You made a way for me, O Sa - viour,
G2
Bm7
Asus4
G2
Bm7
I'm Yours for - e - ver more. I'm Yours for - e - ver more.

PUTTING ON LOVE

Based on Colossians 3

You are God's chosen people,
holy and supremely loved.
So clothe yourselves with
gentleness, with humility and
with patience.
Above all put on love
Let love bind us together in
perfect unity.

Show tolerance to one another
and forgive your hurts,
Know that the Lord has forgiven
you with grace, with endurance
and with kindness.
Above all put on love
Let love bind us together in
perfect unity.

Let Christ's peace rule in your
hearts and as you sing hymns
and spiritual songs,
Let your hearts be filled with
compassion, with contentment
and with joy.
Above all put on love
Let love bind us together in
perfect unity.

Sue Rinaldi

Vocal-Wise

X Factor, Pop Idol and Popstar to Operastar have captured the awareness of millions! An interesting spin-off has been the growing enthusiasm for voice training and so, in the light of this singing revival, how do we recognise our own vocal gift and what can we be doing to develop it!

The voice is a fascinating and expressive instrument. As each human being is unique, so is each voice. You may sound similar to another, but you will never be exactly the same. Be enthusiastic about the voice you have been born with, enjoy it, explore the potential and liberate it!

Vocalist Fit Club

I remember a wonderful singing teacher who asked me to "consider myself an athlete"! For someone who used up every excuse in the book to escape gymnastics at school, this was initially very difficult!! Apparently around 40 muscles are involved in the production of sound; therefore emphasis must be placed on establishing a regular training programme in order to 'work out'. Cultivating the voice also means cultivating the fitness and awareness of your whole body.

You may have a large amount of natural talent, musical intuition and instinct but to get the very best out of your voice, this has to be combined with training and exercise. As you delve into the vocal world, you will become diaphragm-aware, vocal cord-sensitive and posture-positive as you catalogue the advice from the wise.

This Is The Air I Breathe

1. Similar to an athlete, it is important to warm up before singing. Failure to do so may damage your voice and affect performance! Deep breathing exercises are very good at getting body and breathing muscles working. "The foundation for good singing is breath control", says voice guru Tona de Brett. A singer must have the ability to intake an adequate supply of breath and control the escape, supplying enough breath at the right pressure to support the voice.

2. It is easy to spot singers with a bad breathing technique! The 'give away' signs are an inability to sing through the line, wavering off towards the end on low volume; or an inability to support high and low notes and as a result the tuning wavers; or inappropriate intakes of breath during a line at an obviously wrong place!

3. Regular exercises enable singers to develop their breathing mechanism. The pear-shaped lungs are wider at the bottom than at the top and generally only the narrow, upper part of the lungs is used. The art of using the base of the lungs needs to be developed – this area is often referred to as the powerhouse! Remember that as your lungs are filling up, the shoulders must not move upwards!

4. Stand up comfortably without slouching and take a deep breath. If this is done properly, the dome-shaped diaphragm muscle will be pushed out. As you then breathe out, the muscle pushes back in. Practice this rhythmically. There are many different breathing exercises to choose from - just practice them regularly.

5. Simple exercises help. Even as you walk around, count to four and breathe in, hold for four and breathe out for four. As you practice this, extend the count. Singing scales is also excellent practice.

Explore

There is a lot to learn and a lot to remember! If you are serious about developing your voice, consideration must also be given to word articulation, agility, microphone technique and interpretation to name but a few! Good singing is also dependant on overall health and fitness and even your daily food intake comes under the microscope for examination! There are also distinctive learning points relating to live performance and studio recording.

How much time you devote to training your voice depends on your goals and aspirations! But there is a wonderful reward. Your voice unlocks more than a melody or a lyric. It also becomes a channel for communicating an emotion of the spirit, a glimpse into the soul, and finds a resting place in the ears and hearts of the listeners. Now, isn't that rewarding!!

Sue Rinaldi

Visits music teams, churches, creative schools with the 'Voice Factory'

53. LOVE THAT WILL NOT LET ME GO
(All that I need)

Helen Gallagher

This song is recorded on the Spring Harvest 'Perfect Sacrifice - New Songs 2009' and 'Acoustic Worship' albums

Last time to Coda
Asus4 A G D/F♯ A/C♯ Bm G2
I am sa - tis - fied as long as You are near:
Em7 A
1.
D A/C♯
You are my ev - 'ry - thing.
Bm A
D.C.
2.
D Em7 D/F♯
D.S.
In You
Coda
Em7 A D A/C♯
You are my ev - 'ry - thing.
Bm A D

54. MAY THE LORD BLESS YOU

Sam Hargreaves

G2 Bm7 Asus4 A G2 Bm7
and show you grace,
and show you love,
1. Asus4 A
2. Asus4 A D
and give you hope,
and give you peace.

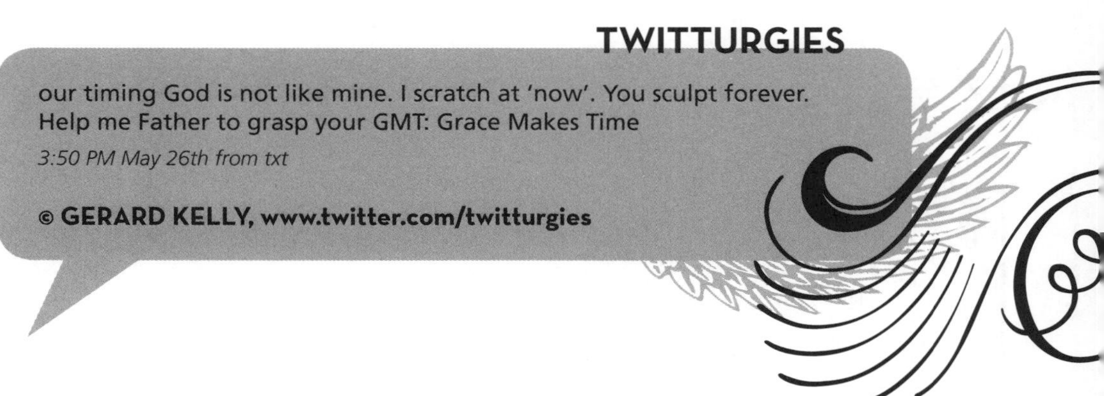
TWITTURGIES
our timing God is not like mine. I scratch at 'now'. You sculpt forever. Help me Father to grasp your GMT: Grace Makes Time
3:50 PM May 26th from txt
© GERARD KELLY, www.twitter.com/twitturgies

55. MEEKNESS AND MAJESTY

(This is your God)

Graham Kendrick

Am F F♯dim7 C Am Dm
ma-jes-ty. Bow down and wor-ship for
G B♭2 F G
this is your God, this is your
1.,2.
A♭ Gm7 C
God.
Last time
B♭2
God,
F G A♭ Gm7 C
this is your God.

56. MORE THAN JUST ANOTHER SONG

(Listening)

Vicky Beeching

Thougthtfully, building

D/C♯
Bm9
'cause we don't want to miss a whis - per, Je - sus, now we
to seek the One whose love has sought me, gaz - ing on Your
G2
Em
Dmaj7/F♯
G2
lean in clo - ser, and we wait.
shin - ing beau - ty all my days.
(So)
Chorus
Last time to Coda
Aadd4
Bm7
G2
Aadd4
Bm7
Speak, Lord, Your ser - vants are list - 'ning, Your ser - vants are list -
G2
1.
Aadd4
Bm9
G2
Aadd4
Bm7
'ning.
D.C. (v.2)
2.
Mid section
G2
Aadd4
Bm9
G2
2. Lord, I want to
What is on Your heart, O God, to - day?

IN THE SILENCE

In the silence,
when the name of God is never mentioned,
still, he is present.

In the boardroom,
when the name of God is never spoken
except in angry curse,
he is present
when his people live out
his generosity.

In the government room,
where the values of God
are sidelined
by those whom God appointed,
he is present
when his people live out
his justice.

In the bedroom,
where the daughters of God
are abused
by those who should protect,
he is present
when his people live out his faithfulness.

In the classroom,
when the story God is never told
except as a myth or fable,
he is present
when his children live out
his wisdom.

In the silence
the still, small voice calls out
your name.

MY GOD IS GOOD

57.

Pete & Nicki Sims

G
D/F♯
G
faith - ful to de - li - ver on ev - 'ry pro - mise He has made;
migh - ty to de - li - ver, he will keep You safe from harm,
D
G
D/F♯
when I'm walk - ing through the val - ley I don't
by the pow - er of the Spi - rit and the
Em7
Asus4
A
Bridge
G
have to be a - fraid. His love ne - ver fails,
stretch - ing of his arm.
A
G/B
A/C♯
oh, His love ne - ver fails, no, His
G
Em7
A
Asus4
A
D.C.
love ne - ver fails, this I know.

Mid section
D
G
Asus4 A
D/F♯
Through joy and through pain, he stays the same.
G
Asus4 A
D/F♯
Sea - sons may change, his love re-mains.
G
Cmaj7
A/C♯
D7
Through joy and through pain, he stays the same.
G
Em7
Asus4 A
D/F♯
G
Sea-sons may change, his love re-mains. For
D.C. (al fine)
Em
D
C
Asus4 A
e - ver - more I will pro - claim.

58. MY LORD, WHAT LOVE IS THIS

(Amazing love)

Graham Kendrick

With strength

F
A
the Son of God given for me. My
Am7
Am/G
D
Am7
debt he pays, and my death he dies, that I
D
Am7
1.,2.
G
D
might live, that I might live.
G/D
D
A/D
3.
D
2. And
3. And
might live,
rall.
Am7
G
D
that I might live.

59. MY TIMES ARE IN YOUR HANDS

(I will hold on)

Nigel Briggs

Csus4(A)
F2/B♭(D)
fall, You help me stand.
Csus4(A)
E - ven when I'm lost, You take my hand.
F2/B♭(D)
Chorus
F(D)
I will hold on,
3rd time to Coda 1
F/B♭(D)
Dm7(Bm)
I will hold on, I will hold on,
Last time to Coda 2
C(A)
F/B♭(D)
1.
D.C.
2.
D.S.
yes, I will trust in You. I will hold

Coda 1
Dm7(Bm)
C(A)
F/B♭(D)
on.
F(D)
F/B♭(D)
Dm7(Bm)
C(A)
F/B♭(D)
D.S.S. al Coda 2
Coda 2
F/B♭(D)
F(D)

NOTHING CAN SEPARATE 60.

(Your love never fails)

C
G
D
C
Chorus
You stay the same
G
D/F♯
Am
G/B
through the a - ges;
Your love ne - ver chang-
C
G
D/F♯
- es.
There may be pain in the night,
but joy comes with the morn-
Am
C
G
D/F♯
- ing.
And when the o - ceans rage
I don't have
Am
G/B
C
G
D/F♯
to be a-fraid
be-cause I know that You love me
and Your

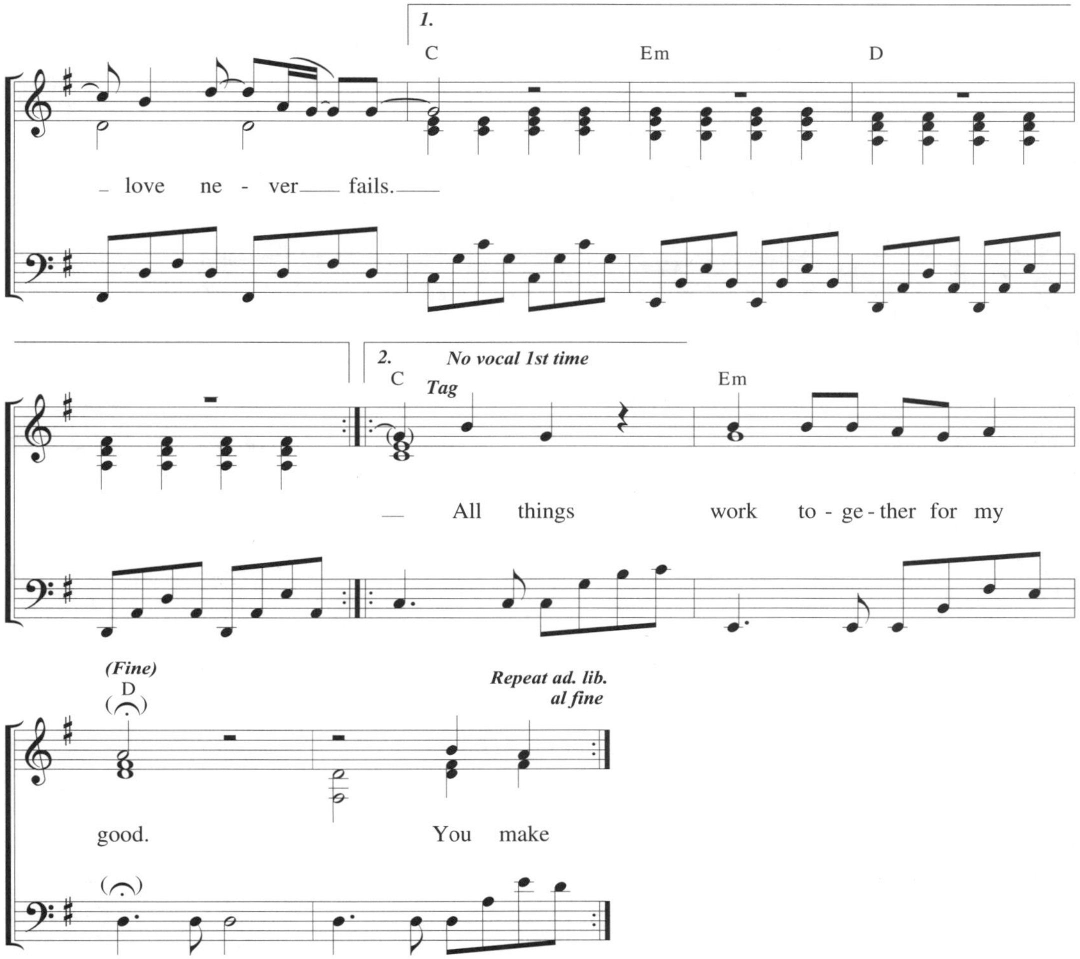

1.

C Em D

love ne - ver fails.

2. *No vocal 1st time*

C Em

Tag

All things work to - ge - ther for my

(Fine)

D

Repeat ad. lib. al fine

good. You make

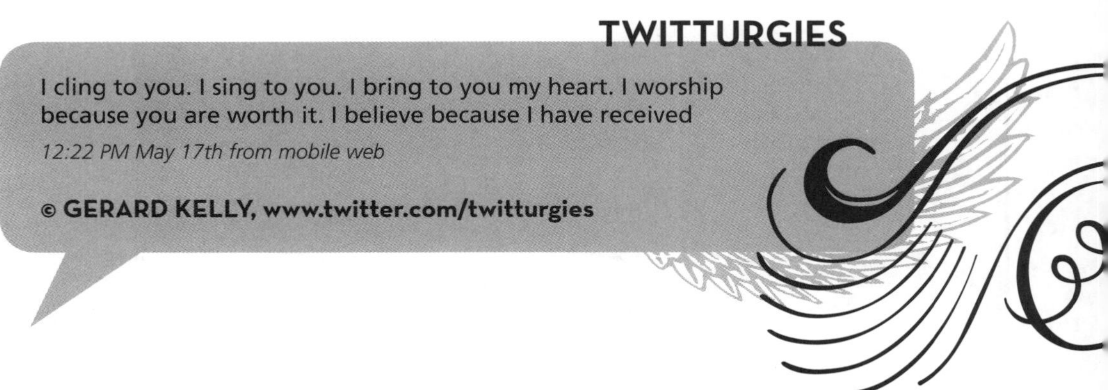

61. NOW UNTO THE KING WHO REIGNS OVER ALL

(How great is Your faithfulness)

Jonas Myrin
& Matt Redman

This song is recorded on the Spring Harvest 'Glory - New Songs 2010' album

A(G) E/G♯ (D) F♯m(Em) D(C) A(G) E(D)
- vens ring, the saints all sing, 'Great is Your faith - ful-ness.'
F♯m(Em) D(C) A(G) E/G♯ (D) F♯m(Em) D(C)
From age to age we will pro-claim,
Last time to Coda
1.
A(G) E(D) F♯m(Em) D(C) A(G) E(D)
'Great is Your faith - ful-ness, how great is Your faith - ful-ness.'
D.C.(v.2)
2.,4.
D.S. (al Coda)
A(G) E/G♯(D) F♯m(Em) A(G) E/G♯(D) F♯m(Em) F♯m(Em) D(C)
Yes, the hea -
3.
F♯m(Em) D(C) A(G) E(D) A(G)
Mid section
how great is Your faith - ful-ness.' From

D(C) A(G) E(D) F♯m(Em) D(C) A(G) E(D)
ge - ne-ra - tion to ge - ne-ra - tion, You nev - er fail us, O God.
D(C) A(G) E(D) F♯m(Em) G(F)
Yes - ter-day and to-day and to-mor - row, un - til the day You re-turn.
D.S. Coda
Esus4(D) E(D) F♯m(Em) D(C) A(G) E(D)
The hea - 'How great is Your faith - ful-ness,
F♯m(Em) D(C) A(G) E(D) A(G) A2(G)
how great is Your faith - ful-ness.'

OH, HOW COULD IT BE

62.

(Remembrance)

Matt Redman & Matt Maher
Mid section words: taken from the English translation of the Memorial Acclamation from The Roman Missal

This song is recorded on the Spring Harvest 'Glory - New Songs 2010' album

D Bm7 A G D
mem - ber You, and re-mem - brance leads us to wor -
A G D A
- ship. And as we wor - ship You, our wor -
Last time to Coda
G D A Em7 D/F♯
- ship leads to com-mu - nion. We re-spond to Your in-vi-ta -
G Bm7 A
1.
D Dmaj7 Em7
- tion; we re-mem - ber You.
D.C.(v.2)
2.
D
Mid section
2. See His You. Dy-ing, You de -

G A D G A
stroyed our death. Ris-ing, You re-stored our
Bm A
life. Lord Je-sus, come in glo-ry, Lord Je-sus, come in
G 1. D 2.
glo-ry. Dy-ing, You de- Lord Je-sus, come in
D Dmaj7 Em7 D.S. al Coda
glo-ry. By Your mer-
Coda
G Em7 D/F♯ G Bm7 A D
-tion, we re-spond to Your in-vi-ta-tion; we re-mem-ber You.

63. O PRECIOUS SIGHT

(The wonder of the cross)

Capo 1(G)

Vicky Beeching

Steadily

This song is recorded on the Spring Harvest 'Journey - Live Worship 2009', 'Acoustic Worship', 'He is risen indeed' and Wonderful Saviour - New Songs 2008' albums

Eb/G(D) Bbm7(Am) Ab(G) Fm7(Em)
ne - ver lose the won-der, the won - der of the cross. May I see it like the
Eb/G(D) Bbm7(Am) Fm7(Em) Db(C)
first time, stand ing as a sin - ner lost. Un-done by mer - cy and left
Ab/C(G) Bbm7(Am) Fm7(Em) Db(C) Eb/G(D)
speech - less, watch ing wide - eyed at the cost. May I ne - ver lose the
(Fine)
Fm7(Em) Bbm(Am) Eb/G(D) Ab(G)
D.C. al fine
won - der, the won - der of the cross. 3. Be - hold, the

64. ONCE I WAS DEAD TO YOU

(Promised land)

Lou and Nathan Fellingham & busbee

Last time to Coda
G
suff - 'ring I'm for - gi - ven, pres - sing on - ward to the
Je - sus, sent from hea - ven to take us home - ward to the
1.,3.
C D
pro - mised land. 2. Sent from His
3. Now with the
4.
C D
D.S. (Last chorus)
pro - mised land. His name is
2.
C D C
Mid section
G D A
pro - mised land. You've bought me with a price, a per - fect sac - ri - fice.
C G D C G
Now all I have I give to You. My life no long - er mine,
D A C G
D.S. Coda
C D
to live or die is Christ. Bound now for hea - ven. What a pro - mised land.

65. OPEN MY EYES

(My soul sings)

Stuart Garrard, Martin Smith
& Jonathan Thatcher

Slowly

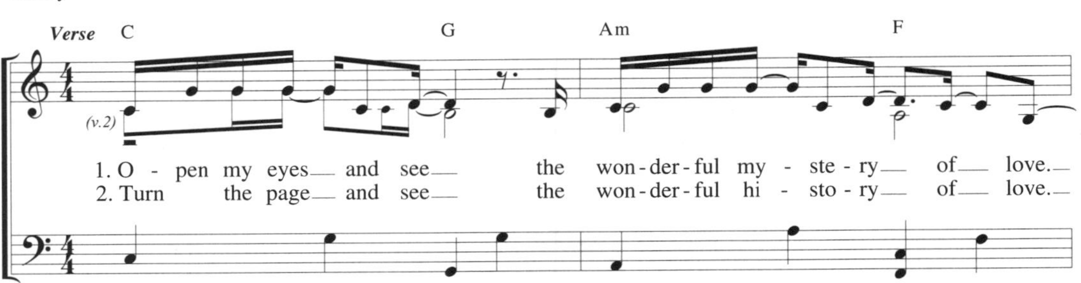

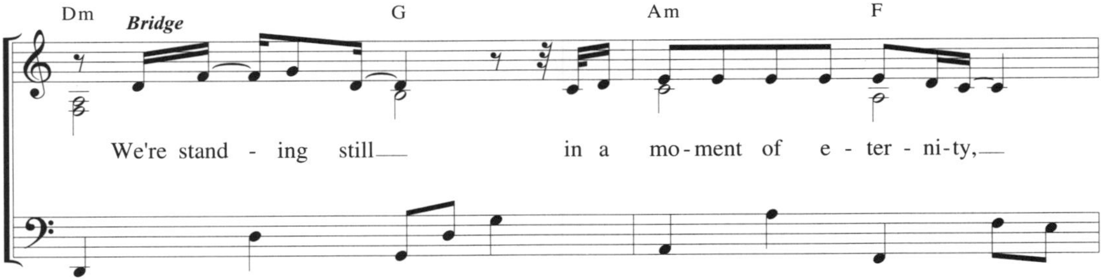

Dm G Am G/B
where worlds collide, and I feel the breath of hea - ven o - ver me.
C Chorus G Am F 3
My soul sings, my soul sings, my soul sings how I love You.
2nd time D.S.
C G/D C/E F 3
My soul sings my soul sings, my soul sings how I love You.
1. C Dm7 C/E F
2. C

66. ON THE DARK NIGHT

(Emmanuel God with us)

Vicky Beeching

Dsus2(C)
Chorus
E/G♯(D)
D/F♯(C)
Em - ma - nu - el, You're God with us, and we re - mem - ber You
Dsus2(C)
A2/C♯(G)
E/G♯(D)
through Your bo - dy and Your blood. Em - ma - nu - el,
D/F♯(C)
Last time to Coda
Dsus2(C)
You gave Your life, our hearts cry thank - You for Your sa - cri -
1.
F♯m9(Em)
Dmaj9(C)
A2(G)
E/G♯(D)
D.C. (v.2)
- fice.
2.
Bm(Am)
F♯m7(Em)
Dsus2(C)
- fice. Ooo.

A(G)
Esus4(D) E(D)
Bm(Am)
F♯m(Em)
Let Your blood co-ver me, wash me white and set me free;
D2(C)
1.,2.
A(G)
E/G♯(D)
3.
A(G)
E/G♯(D)
let Your blood make me clean to-day, to-day.
day, to-day.
D.S. al Coda
Coda
Bm7(Am)
A/C♯(G)
D(C)
D(C)
E(D)
D2(C)
Em-ma-nu-el, You for Your sa-cri-fice.

SEARCH MY HEART

Pre - cious are Your thoughts to me, O God, Your ho -
E(no3rd)
D
- ly, Your right - eous ways; lead me in Your e - ver - last - ing love,
Bm7
A
E
Fa - ther a - bove, I will serve You all my days. And
A
E
if I climb up to the moun - tain tops, I know I will find You there;
D
Bm7
if e - ver to the val - ley I go, when my heart is low, You lift

A E D Bm7 E
me from de - spair. And Your ban-ner o-ver me is love,
D Bm7 E
yeah, Your ban-ner o-ver me is love, Your
D Bm7 E A Asus4 A
ban-ner o-ver me is love, is love.
Asus4 A
D.C.

68. SEE MARTHA WEEPING AT A TOMB

(God of compassion)

Simon Brading
& Graham Kendrick

This song is recorded on the Spring Harvest 'Glory - New Songs 2010' album

1.
D.C.(v.2)
2.,3.
Am
Am7
Am
Je - sus comes.
falls face - down in her
lift our eyes, look in -
(v.3)
(v.3)
C
Em
D
deep de - spair, pours out her pain, and his heart breaks. Then his
to the face of a God who knows, of a God who weeps. And his
(v.3)
Am
C
an - ger burns in the face of death: Je - sus
voice cries out, in the dark - est place: I am the Life,
Chorus
G/D
D
Am7
weeps, Je - sus weeps. God of com - pas - sion,
I am the Life.

C/G
C
G
D
God of com - pas-sion is here.
God of all
Am7
C/G
C
G
Last time to Coda
com - fort
is here with us,
has come to us;
1.
D
Em
D
Em
D
God of com - pas - sion.
D.C.(v.3)
2.
C
G/B
C
G/B
D
G/B
And
Mid section
C
G/B
C
G/D
now
he
lives,
he is the life,
he is the life.

Bm
C
G/B
C
– A - live in___ him, we'll ne - ver die,_
1.
2.
D.S. al Coda
G/D
Bm
G/B
Bm
– ne - ver die.___ And___ – God of com -
Coda
D
Em
D
Em
___ God of com - pas - sion.
C
G/B
C
Em
D
Em
C
G/B
C

69. THE GOD WHO SET THE STARS IN SPACE

Words: Timothy Dudley-Smith
Tune: from Wurttemberg Gesangbuch,1784
arr. David Peacock

G
C
D7
life should flour - ish and a - bound be - neath its Ma - ker's
all that God cre - a - ted fair pol - lu - ted and un -
hu - man greed and con - flict cease and all be re - con
lon - ger, Lord, be - tray your trust but prove cre - a - tion's
a - tion's songs shall rise as one and God be glo - ri -
1. - 4.
5.
G
C/G
G
G
hand.
clean.
ciled.
friend.
2. A
3. O
4. Re -
5. Our
fied.

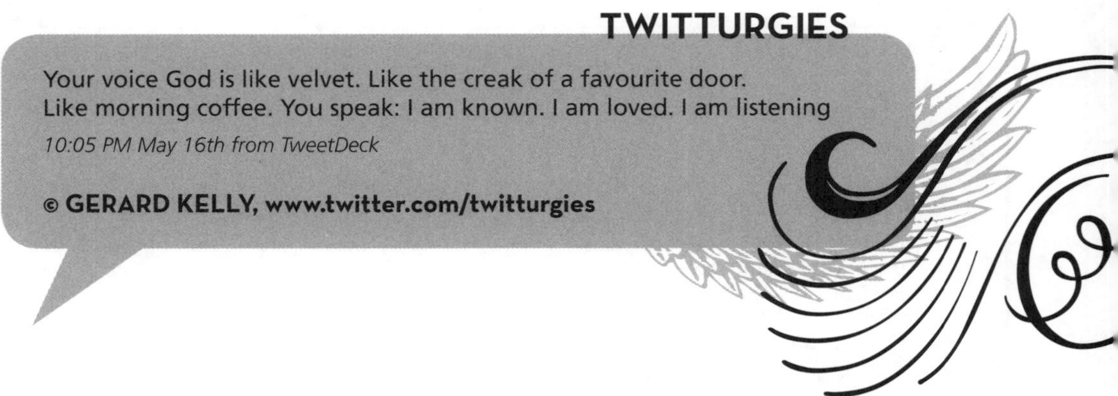
TWITTURGIES
Your voice God is like velvet. Like the creak of a favourite door.
Like morning coffee. You speak: I am known. I am loved. I am listening
10:05 PM May 16th from TweetDeck
© GERARD KELLY, www.twitter.com/twitturgies

70. THERE IS AN EVERLASTING KINDNESS

(The compassion hymn)

Keith and Kristyn Getty
& Stuart Townend

1.
G D/F♯ A Bm7 A/C♯ D
2.,3.,4.
D
Chorus
rest.
2. And with com -
near. What
thief.
Christ.
A A/G D/F♯ G
bound - less love, what fa - thom - less grace You have
day we live an of - f'ring of praise as we
Em7 D/F♯ G
1.
A Bm7 A/C♯ D
shown us, O God of com - pas - sion. Each
show to the world Your com -
2.
A7sus4 G D/F♯ A Bm7 A/C♯ D
- pas - sion.
G D/F♯ A Bm7 A/C♯
1.,2.
D
D.C.
3.
D
3. We stood be -
4. How beau - ti -

THERE IS LOVE

(Stronger)

Reuben Morgan
& Ben Fielding

Last time to Coda
1.
C
G
F
G
Fmaj7
G
C/E
Cmaj7
writ - ten: 'Christ is ri - sen'. Je - sus, You are Lord of all.
Fmaj7
G
C/E
C
2.
F
Am
C/E
G/B
3. No be - all.
F
Am
C/E
G/B
Mid section
G
F
So let Your name be lift - ed high - er,
1.,2.,3.
4.
D.S. al Coda
Am7
G
C
G
G
be lift - ed high - er, be lift - ed high - er. So let Your name You are
Coda
F
all.

72. THERE'S A NEW DAY DAWNING

(Jubilee)

Nigel Briggs
& Trent

1.
2.,3.
Chorus
G
2. It's a
It's time to live the life,
C
Em
Bm
for God's church to shine for Christ;
C
oh, tell the world of love
G
D/F♯
Em
oh, be - yond this flesh and blood,
Last time to Coda
C
Am7
oh, it's time to live the life.

G
C/G
1.
D.C.
2.
1. There's a
1° Repeat x 8, building then D.S. al Coda
2° Repeat x 2 al fine
Mid section
(Fine)
(D.S.S.) o - pen the win - dows of hea-ven, let Your love shine through, till the world knows You.
G
C
Oh, oh, oh, oh. (It's time)
Coda
C
Am7
yes, it's time to live the life.
G
C
D.S.S. al fine
So

THIS IS OUR SONG

(Now and ever)

73.

Nigel Briggs
& Trent

E
D2
This is our
2. Chorus
A
E
Je - sus is a - live to - day, see his sav - ing
Je - sus o - pened up the way with truth that ne - ver
D
1.
A
grace, now and e - ver.
fades:
2.
Last time to Coda
1.
D.C.
2.
he'll reign for - e - ver. This is our
F♯m
Mid section
E
Came to earth to be with us, con - quered death up -

D
A
on a cross,
Son of God, the ri-sen One; You're now and
e - ver.
F♯m
O-pened eyes and hearts set free,
E
D
showed the world its de - sti-ny,
Je-sus Christ, the
Bm
D
liv-ing King, You're now and e - ver.
Coda
D
A

74. THROUGH IT ALL

Matt Redman
& Jonas Myrin

Bridge
D♯m/A♯(Bm)
F♯m(Dm)
E(C)
You nev - er turn or change, You nev - er break
Em7(Cm)
B/D♯(G)
F♯m(Dm)
the faith, yes - ter - day, to - day and al - ways.
E2(C)
Chorus
C♯m(Am)
G♯m(Em)
F♯(D)
Through it all You are faith - ful. Through it all,
C♯m(Am)
G♯m(Em)
F♯(D)
C♯m(Am)
G♯m(Em)
You are strong. As we walk through the sha -
F♯(D)
E2(C)
G♯m(Em)
1.
F♯(D)
dows, still You shine on. Still You shine on.

E2(C)
G♯m(Em)
F♯(D)
D.S.(v.2)
2.
D.S.S.
F♯(D)
Through it all
3.,4.
F♯(D)
E(C)
G♯m(Em)
F♯(D)
Mid section
Still You shine on.
You are
E(C)
B(G)
F♯(D)
C♯m(Am)
G♯m(Em)
faith - ful,
Je - sus, You are
faith - ful to the end.
1.,3.-5.
F♯(D)
2.
F♯(D)
D.S.S.
6.
F♯(D)
You are
Through it all
You ne - ver turn
F♯m(Dm)
E(C)
Em7(Cm)
B(G)
or change,
You nev - er break
the faith.

TO GIVE AS YOU GAVE

75.

(Here on the earth)

Last time to Coda
F♯(D)
B(G)
here on the earth.
Give us eyes to see,
F♯/A♯(D)
E(C)
the cou-rage to be-lieve
here on the earth,
3rd time D.S. al Coda
F♯/A♯(D)
1.
E2(C)
2.
Bsus4(G)
B(G)
here on the earth.
E(C)
Mid section
F♯(D)
G♯m(Em)
Bring-ing jus-tice,
lov-ing mer-cy,
walk-ing hum-bly
1.
D♯m(Bm)
2.
D♯m(Bm)
E2(C)
with our God.
with our God.

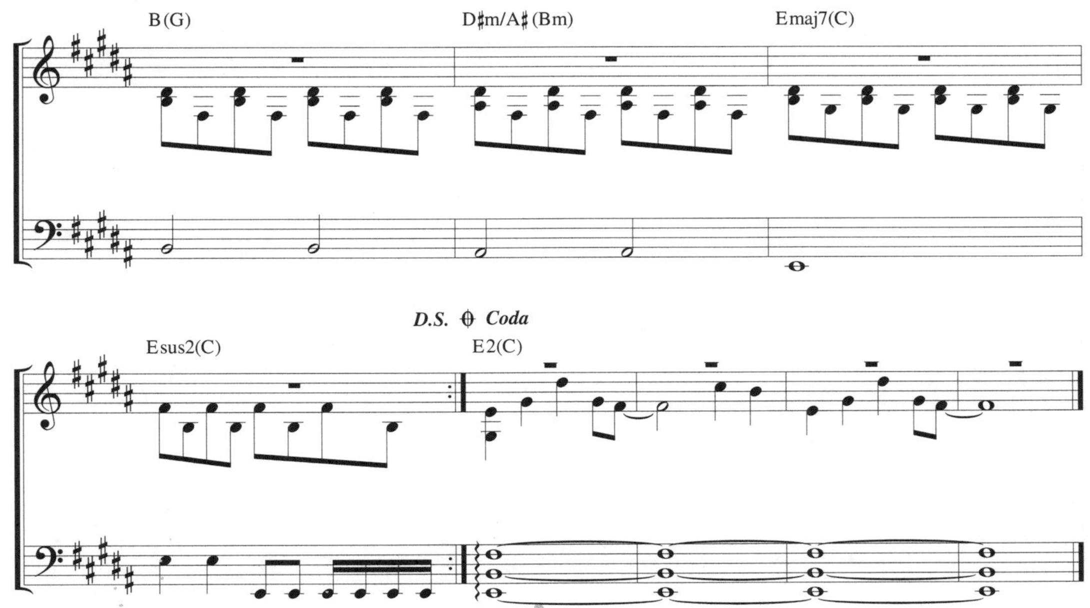

RENEWING OUR MINDS

Engaging with our minds,
our eyes focussed on Jesus
and our hearts aware of the
struggle on earth.

"Lead us, Lord!" we cry
as we try to untangle
the slippery spaghetti of ethics
today.

Where do we start?
Where do we stop?
Is there an anchor, a pivot point?

Lord Jesus, we need your grace,
your humour,
your love and your wisdom
to keep talking to each other.

Please keep us talking,
keep us loving,
keep our eyes on you
and our hearts in touch with your
world.

Amen.

76. TO SEE THE KING OF HEAVEN FALL

(Gethsemane)

Keith Getty
& Stuart Townend

Thoughtfully

Gsus2 G Em7 F♯m7
1. B(no3rd)
2. Bm Bm/A Gmaj7 D/F♯
Yours, yet not my will but Yours.' 2. To paid.
paid, and ev - 'ry sin is
all, the Sa - viour drank it
Em7 Dmaj7 C♯m7(♭5) F♯/E Bm/D F♯m/A Gmaj7 D/F♯ Em7 Dmaj7 F♯7sus4 F♯7
3. What
3. Gsus2 G Em7 F♯m7 B(no3rd)
all, the Sa - viour drank it all.

77.

TO YOU, O LORD

Graham Kendrick

This song is recorded on the Spring Harvest 'No-one Like You - iScape 2006' album

A♯dim
A
F♯m7
oh, how I need You. To You I lift up my soul, to You I lift up my soul.
Last time to Coda
A/B
B 7
E
B/E
A/E
E
B/E
A/E
D.C. (v.2)
E
B/E
A/E
E
B/E
3. Re-mem-ber, Lord, your mer-cy and love, that e-ver flow
A/E
E
B/E
A/E
E
from of old. Re-mem-ber not the sins of my youth,
B/E
A2/E
or my re-bel-li-ous ways. Ac-cord-ing to Your

A E A
love, re - mem - ber me. Ac - cord - ing to Your love,
F♯m7 B7sus4 B7 B7sus4 B7 D.S. al Coda
for You are good, O Lord.
Coda
E B/E A/E E B/E
To you, O Lord, I lift up my soul. To You, O my Lord,
A/E 1. E 2. E
I lift up my soul. To You, O Lord,

TO YOUR THRONE WE'RE WELCOME NOW 78.

(The cross is still speaking today)

Ben Jones

This song is recorded on the Spring Harvest 'Glory - New Songs 2010' album

F#7
Bm
Chorus
_ whole.
_ paid.
The cross is still speak-ing to-
G
D
F#7
day, the cross is still mak-ing a way for us to
Bm
G
wor - ship You. Draw near to the most ho-ly place, draw
D
F#7
near with our hearts full of praise, now to wor - ship
1.
Bm
C#m/B
F#7
Bm
You, we wor - ship You.

D.C. (v.2)
2.
Tag
C♯m/B
F♯7
Bm
You.
You're the
Bm
G
Lord of this life, You're the King of this heart, You're ev - 'ry - thing I could want,
D
F♯7
all I de - sire; You are Lord,
You are Lord.
To repeat
Last time
Bm
You're the

79. WE BOW OUR HEARTS

(Adoration)

With adoration

Brenton Brown

This song is recorded on the Spring Harvest 'Perfect Sacrifice - New Songs 2009' album

1.,4.
D.C. (v.2)
3.
D.S. al fine
Em
Em7
C
(Fine)
C
You are.
2. We
Re-ceive our a-do-
2.
C
Mid section
D
Ev-'ry soul You've saved sings out. Ev-'ry thing You've
an-gel's song. We're ga-thered to Your
C
G
D
made re-sounds. All cre-a-tion's stand-ing now, lift-ing up
an-cient throne. Chil-dren in our Fa-ther's arms, shout-ing out
1.
2.
D.S.
C
your name.
Your praise.
We're caught up in the
Re-ceive our a-do-

80. WE SING A SONG OF SAVING GRACE

(Saving grace)

Neil Bennets
& Eoghan Heaslip

Chorus
A
wor - ship.
Praise, praise,
Praise, praise,
E/G♯
praise, lift your hands to hea - ven, for His love
praise to our God for e - ver, for the glo -
D
1.
A/C♯
F♯m
has res - cued us from the sha - dow of the grave.
ry of His Name,
E
2.
A/C♯
D
we sing the song
Last time to Coda
E/G♯
1.
A
E/G♯
A
of sav - ing grace.

D.C.(v.2)
2.
Mid section
E/G♯
D
grace. A love stron - ger than death
A/C♯
F♯m
has lift - ed our heads; and
E
D
we find peace in the pre - sence of God. Love
A/C♯
D
high - er than moun - tains still is the rea - son we sing,
A/C♯
D2
the rea - son we love You.

A CENTERING PRAYER

Grant us discernment that we may know what is best as we live to serve you.
Help us to fix our eyes on you, Jesus,
And fill us with the fruit of righteousness.

Grant us love that we may abound in knowledge and in depth of insight.
Help us to fix our eyes on you, Jesus,
And fill us with the fruit of righteousness.

Grant us direction that you will continue to be at the centre of our lives.
Help us to fix our eyes on you, Jesus,
And fill us with the fruit of righteousness.

Grant us joy and certain faith that we may be able to stand firm in the one Spirit.
Help us to fix our eyes on you, Jesus,
And fill us with the fruit of righteousness.

Grant us forgiveness that we may be pure and blameless until the day of Christ.
Help us to fix our eyes on you, Jesus,
And fill us with the fruit of righteousness.

81. WE GIVE GLORY AND PRAISE

Matt Osgood

F♯m
E
D
A
Esus4
the awe-some tri-ni - ty. For-e - ver Fa - ther, Spi - rit, Son.
E
A/C♯
D
A
F♯m
You are, You were and al - ways will be God from e -
Last time to Coda
E
D
A
Esus4
ter - ni - ty; for - e - ver three, for - e - ver one.
1.
E
D
A
Esus4
You are our God, You are our God.
D.C. (v.3)
2. Mid section
E
E
Bm7
A/C♯
3. We give You are our God, You are our God.

D2 E Bm7 A/C♯
You are our God, You are our God.
D2 E Bm7 A/C♯
The only God, You are, the living God,
D2 E D/F♯
You are, Almighty God, You are,
E/G♯ D2 E
You are our God. You are
D.S. al Coda
Coda
E
You are our God,
D A
You are our God.
1.
E
2.
E
You are our God.

WE WAIT IN HOPE FOR YOU

(Unfailing love)

This song is recorded on the Spring Harvest 'Acoustic Worship' album

B/D♯(G)
E(C)
hope to cling to. Your love is an anchor in the storms of life, for-
Chorus
B(G)
E(C)
e-ver faith-ful. Un-fai-ling love, You
1.
Last time to Coda
B/D♯(G)
C♯m7(Am)
ne-ver let us down. Your pro-mise is a-live.
D.C.
2.
C♯m(Am)
E(C)
We pro-mise is a-live.
G♯m(Em)
Mid section
B/D♯(G)
E(C)
When col-oured dreams fade to grey un-

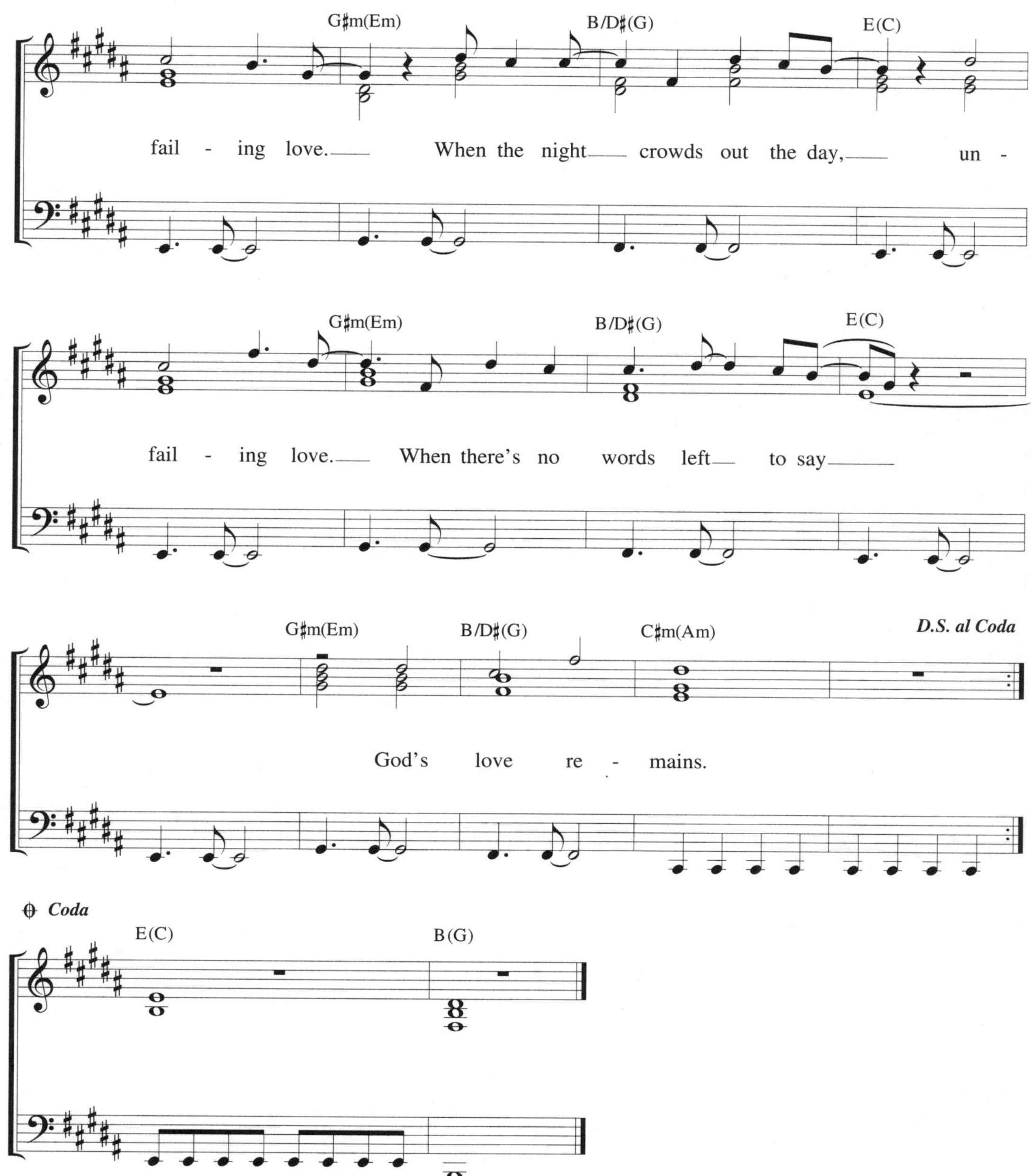
G♯m(Em)
B/D♯(G)
E(C)
fail - ing love. When the night crowds out the day, un -
G♯m(Em)
B/D♯(G)
E(C)
fail - ing love. When there's no words left to say
G♯m(Em)
B/D♯(G)
C♯m(Am)
D.S. al Coda
God's love re - mains.
Coda
E(C)
B(G)

83. WE WERE LOST

(Pardoned)

C♯m/B(Am)
F♯sus4(D)
F♯(D)
seat - ed in the heav'n - ly realms.
know the my - ste - ry of God.
B(G)
C♯m/B(Am)
F♯/B(D)
G♯m(Em)
Re - con - ciled to God, we're for - gi - ven,
Re - ve - la - tion of his wis - dom,
Last time to Coda
2nd & 4th times D.S. (Chorus 2)
B(G)
C♯m/B(Am)
F♯sus4(D)
F♯(D)
B/D♯(G)
E(C)
ne - ver bound by sin a - gain. Praise the King who
shown to us in Je - sus Christ.
B/F♯(G)
F♯(D)
B/D♯(G)
E(C)
B/F♯(G)
saved us through his suff - 'ring, for his life was poured out as an
1st time D.C.(v.2)
F♯(D)
Esus2(C)
F♯(D)
off - 'ring.

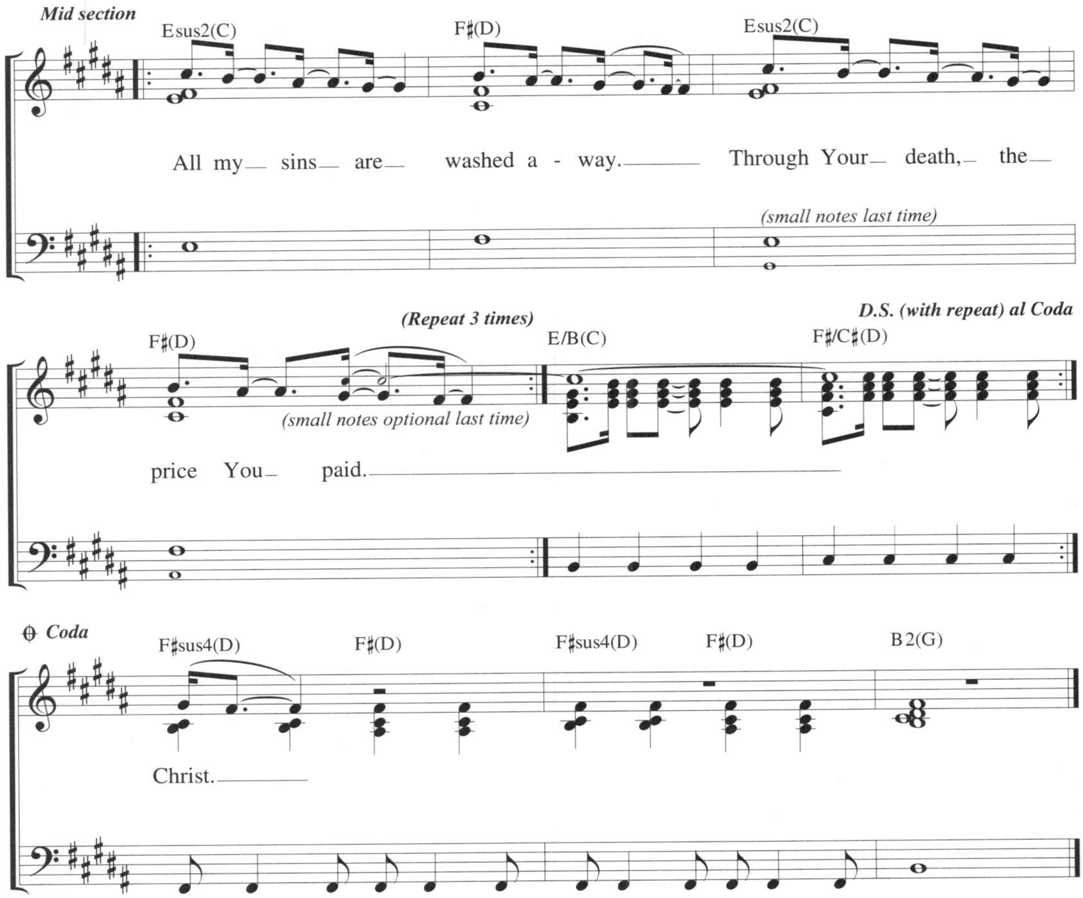

Mid section

Esus2(C) F♯(D) Esus2(C)

All my sins are washed a - way. Through Your death, the

(small notes last time)

(Repeat 3 times) ***D.S. (with repeat) al Coda***

F♯(D) E/B(C) F♯/C♯(D)

(small notes optional last time)

price You paid.

Coda

F♯sus4(D) F♯(D) F♯sus4(D) F♯(D) B2(G)

Christ.

WE WILL DANCE 84.

(For your glory)

A(G)
Let Your name be lift - ed high, as our thank -
E/G♯(D)
G♯m(F♯m)
- ful hearts now cry: 'Je - sus, Je - sus'.
A(G)
Chorus
B(A)
Lift up your heads, you
up a shout to
G♯m7(F♯m)
an - cient gates. Be lift - ed up, you an - cient doors: the
shake the skies. Lift up a cry: 'be glo - ri - fied!' The
A(G)
E(D)
1.,3.,5.
King is com - ing in, the King is com - ing in. We lift
King is com - ing in, the King is com - ing in.

2.,6.
D.C.
4.
B(A)
1. We will dance
Mid section
B(A)
We're the people of God with a song to sing, and we're bringing our lives as an offering; we will dance for Your glory, Lord.
cross is the hope that we hold up high, as we tell the whole world of Your love and life; we will dance for Your glo-
A(G)
E(D)
4th time to Coda
B(A)
1.,3.
2.
D.S.
And Your
Lift
Coda
B(A)

85. WE, YOUR CHILDREN, PRAY LORD

(King of the broken)

Capo 1(G)

Steadily, building

Paul Baloche, Steven Curtis-Chapman, Stuart Garrard,
Israel Houghton, Tim Hughes, Graham Kendrick,
Andy Park, Matt Redman, Martin Smith,
Michael W. Smith, Chris Tomlin, Darlene Zschech

Verse

A♭(G) A♭sus4(G) A♭(G) A♭sus4(G) A♭(G) Fm7(Em) E♭/D♭(D) D♭(C) A♭(G) E♭(D)

1. We, Your chil - dren, pray Lord, hum - bly seek Your face; we turn from our sin, Lord, You hear us as we pray.
2. Heal - ing King of na - tions, let your king - dom come. Pu - ri - fy your church, Lord, your glo - ry o - ver us.
3. Lo - ver of the wound - ed, de - fen - der of the weak, friend of the for - got - ten; you wipe a - way our tears.

Bridge

D♭(C) A♭/C(G) E♭(D) Fm7(Em) D♭(C) E♭(D)

Heal us, for - give us, re - store our hearts a - gain. Fill us, breathe up - on us.

Chorus
Last time to Coda
A♭sus4(G) A♭(G) E♭/G(D) Fm7(Em)
Je - sus, Je - sus, Heal - er of na - tions,
(Last chorus)
D♭(C) A♭sus4(G) A♭(G) Cm7(Bm)
Hope of sal - va - tion. Je - sus, Je - sus,
(Last chorus) Hope of the world
(Last chorus)
1.
Fm7(Em) D♭(C)
King of our hearts, King of the bro - ken
(Last chorus) Hope of the world.
A♭(G) A♭sus4(G) A♭(G) A♭sus4(G) A♭(G)
3. D.S. al Coda
2.
D♭(C) B♭m(Am) A♭(G) D♭(C) Fm7(Em)

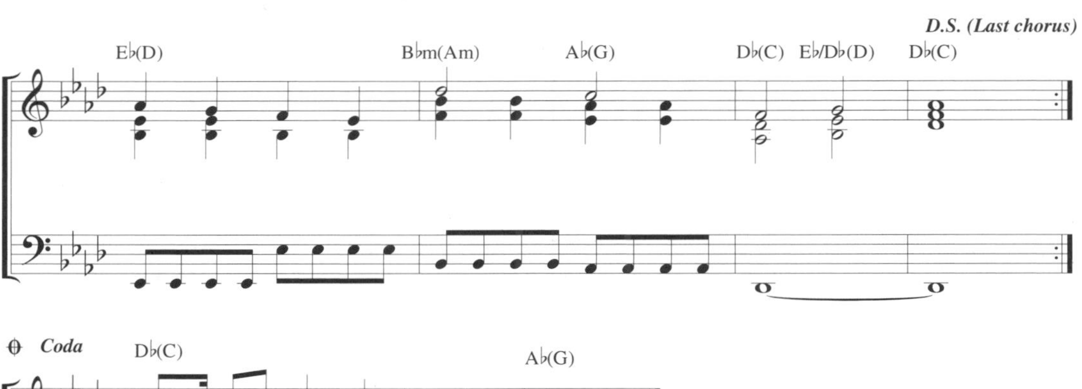
D.S. (Last chorus)
E♭(D)
B♭m(Am)
A♭(G)
D♭(C)
E♭/D♭(D)
D♭(C)

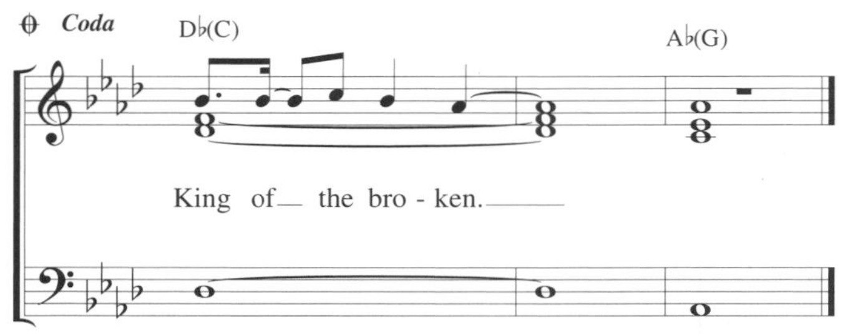
Coda
D♭(C)
A♭(G)
King of the bro - ken.

TWITTURGIES
God let this day be an empty canvas. Write on this blank page your words to be spoken. Your will to be done. Fill this empty space with love
1:47 PM Apr 18th from web
© GERARD KELLY, www.twitter.com/twitturgies

WELCOME, YOU ARE WELCOME

(Inhabit the praise)

86.

Vicky Beeching

Capo 3(C)

B♭(G) Cm(Am) A♭(F) E♭/G(C) B♭(G)
You. Vi - sit us, Lord, You're the one we're long - ing for,
Last time to Coda ⊕
A♭(F) B♭(G) A♭(F) B♭(G) Cm(Am)
Je - sus, You're the one we're long - ing for.
A♭(F) E♭/G(C) B♭(G) Cm(Am)
1. D.C. (v.2)
A♭(F) E♭/G(C)
2. Mid section
A♭(F) E♭/G(C)
Let his
E♭(C)
prai - ses rise, let his prai - ses rise. Let his
Building
E♭(C) B♭/D (G) Cm(Am)
1. - 3.
A♭(F)
4. D.S. al Coda
A♭(F)
prai - ses rise, let his prai - ses rise. Let his

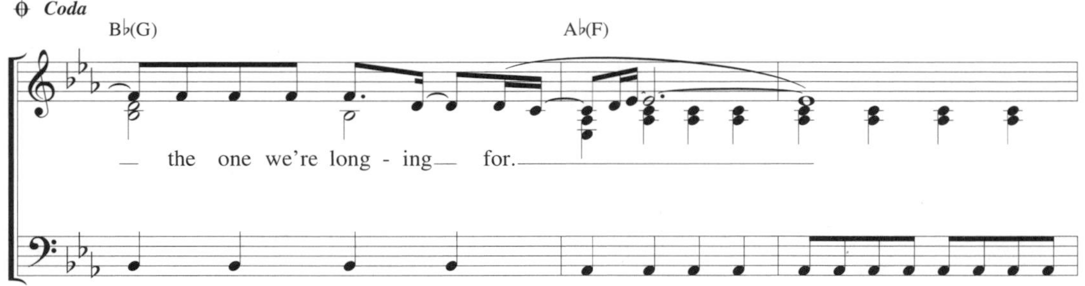

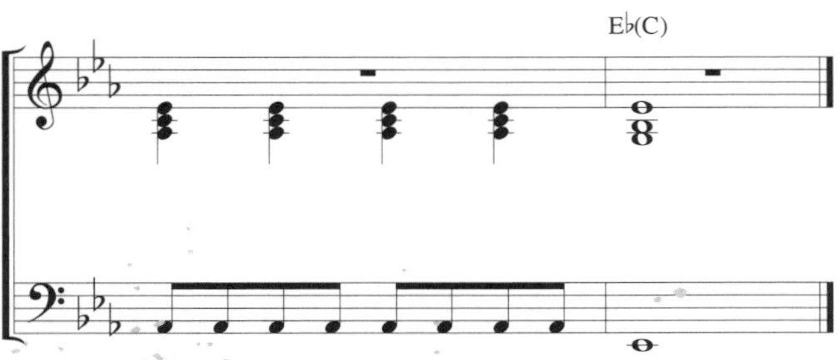

THE CONFLICT

War, exploitation, greed and prejudice – I stand against them all.
I abhor the horror,I recoil from the thought
of atrocities committed in our world …
and I pray for a speedy end to the conflict.

But as I pray, I become conscious
of the conflict within me,
of the anger and prejudice
I feel towards those I don't understand …
and I pray for a speedy end to the conflict.

This conflict within me is shocking.
I abhor the horror,
and recoil from the thought
of atrocities I commit in my heart …
and I pray for a speedy end to the conflict.

I offer the atrocities of my heart,
the conflicts within, to God.
and ask Him to cleanse the thoughts of my heart
by the inspiration of his Holy Spirit,
that I may perfectly love Him … and others. Amen.

87.

WELL, JESUS IS THE ROCK

(Lead me to the rock)

Brian Houston

Capo 1(D)

Rock 'n' roll

This song is recorded on the Spring Harvest 'Glory - New Songs 2010' album

A♭(G)
E♭(D)
soul finds rest in God a - lone: lead me to the Rock that is
thing he has spo - ken, two things I have heard: lead me to the Rock that is
trust in the Lord ev - 'ry day of your life: lead me to the Rock that is
Last time to Coda
(v.2)
(v.3)
F(E)
E♭(D)
A♭(G)
E♭(D)
high - er than I. And he is the place where my hope comes from:
high - er than I. From his strength and his love he gives great re - wards:
high - er than I. And
Chorus
F(E)
E♭(D)
A♭(G)
lead me to the Rock that is high - er than I. Lead me to the One who is
lead me to the Rock that is high - er than I.
E♭(D)
strong and sure, lead me to the One who gives me strength to en - dure.

F(E)
Lead me to the One who teach - es me his ways, and
B♭(A)
D.C. (al Coda)
lead me to the One who loves the sounds of my praise. 3. For my
Coda
E♭(D)
A♭(G)
E♭(D)
in - to his arms You can run and hide: lead me to the Rock that is
B♭7(A)
E♭(D)
high - er than I.

WHAT A MORNING

(Christ is risen indeed)

88.

Matt Boswell

With exuberance

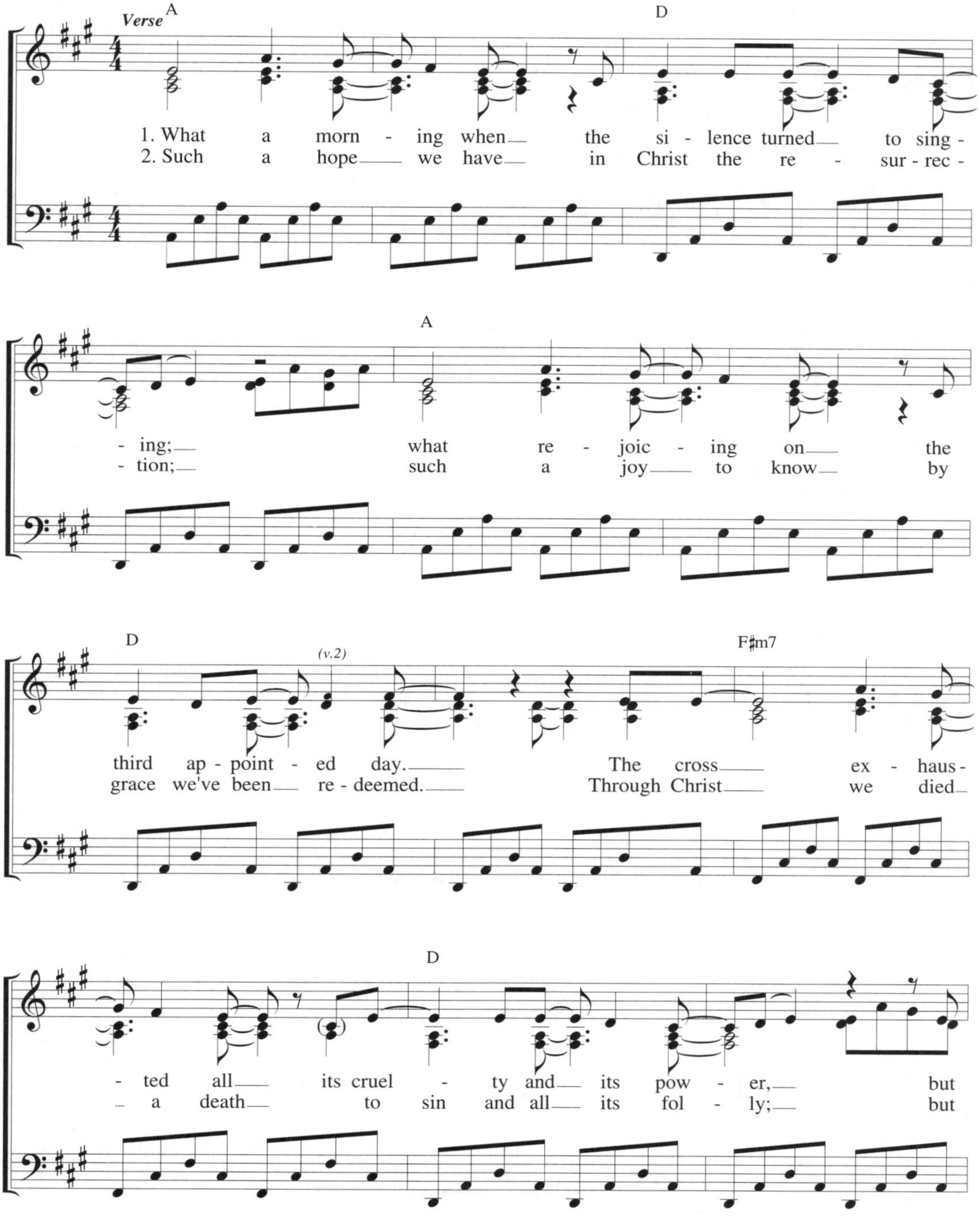

Verse

1. What a morning when the silence turned to sing - ing; what rejoic - ing on the third ap - point - ed day. The cross ex - haus - ted all its cruel - ty and its pow - er, but

2. Such a hope we have in Christ the re - sur - rec - tion; such a joy to know by grace we've been re - deemed. Through Christ we died a death to sin and all its fol - ly; but

This song is recorded on the Spring Harvest 'Glory - New Songs 2010' album

Bm
D
love de-clared its vic - to - ry, and rolled the stone a - way.
glo - ri - fied, we will rise, to live e - ter - nal - ly.
E
Chorus
A
F♯m7
E
D
Christ is ri - sen, He is ri - sen in - deed;
E
D
Death has been de - feat - ed and the grave has lost its sting.
E
A
F♯m7
E
D
Hal - le - lu - jah, with the an - gels we will sing:
3rd time D.S.
Last time to Coda
(3°)
Christ is
Bm
D
E
Christ - is ri - sen, Christ is ris - sen in -

1.
A
Dsus2/A
D.C. (v.2)
deed.
2.
A
Mid section
D
A/C♯
deed.
Sal - va-tion and im-mor - tal praise to
Bm
A/C♯
D
A/C♯
our vic-to - rious King;
Let the hea - vens and the earth with
Bm
A/C♯
D
D.S.
glad ho-san - nas ring.
Christ is
Coda
A
Dsus2
A
deed.

89. WHEN THE SUN IS SHINING

(Jesus is my best friend)

Vicky Beeching
& Wendy Beech-Ward

Exuberantly

This song is recorded on the Spring Harvest 'Journey - Live Worship 2009' album

D
E
F♯m
D
we will be to - ge - ther for-e - ver and e - ver, for-e -
E
F♯m
D
E
F♯m
- ver and e - ver. Sing: ah, oh (ah, oh)
D
E
F♯m
D
ah, oh (ah, oh.) Sing ah, oh
1° D.C. (v.2)
Last time to Coda
E
F♯m
D
E
F♯m
D
Mid section
(ah, oh.) Sing ah, oh (ah, oh.) Je-sus,
D.C. (v.3) al Coda
Coda
E
F♯m
E/G♯
Dsus2
I love You. Je - sus, I love You.

90. WHO IS LIKE THE LORD OUR GOD

(To the praise of Your glory)

Ben Hall
& Nathan Fellingham

E(D)
F♯m7(Em)
C♯m(Bm)
of Your glo - ry we live, we breathe;
B(A)
E(D)
F♯m7(Em)
C♯m(Bm)
tes - ti - fy - ing to You and the life You give.
B(A)
C♯m(Bm)
B/D♯(A)
E(D)
We now set our hope on Christ, lay - ing earth -
A(G)
B(A)
C♯m(Bm)
E(D)
- ly things a - side. We were dead, but You've made
Last time to Coda
1.
D.C. (v.2)
B(A)
A(G)
C♯m(Bm)
E(D)
us a - live.

3. *D.S. al Coda* A(G) | 2. E(D) F♯m7(Em)

— We now set— —

C♯m(Bm) | 1. Bsus4(A) B(A) | 2. Bsus4(A) B(A) *D.S.*

We now set—

𝄌 *Coda*

A(G)

—

TWITTURGIES

We need your guidance God. We need gifts; wisdom; mercy. Miracles.
But more than these, we need your presence.
God our companion draw close

1:09 PM Apr 16th from web

WHO, O LORD, COULD SAVE THEMSELVES 91.

(You alone can rescue)

𝄋
E(C) F♯(D) G♯m(Em) E(C) F♯(D)
res - cue, You a-lone can save. You a-lone can lift us from the grave.
G♯m(Em) E(C) F♯(D) G♯m(Em)
You came down to find us, led us out of death. To You a-lone be-
E(C) F♯(D)
1.
D.C.(v.2)
Bsus4(G) B(G) Bsus4(G) B(G)
longs the high - est praise.
2.,3.
G♯m(Em) E(C) F♯(D) G♯m(Em)
To You a-lone be - longs the high - est praise. To You a-lone be-
E(C) F♯(D) (G) Bsus4 B(G) Bsus4(G) B(G) Bsus4(G) B(G)
longs the high - est praise.

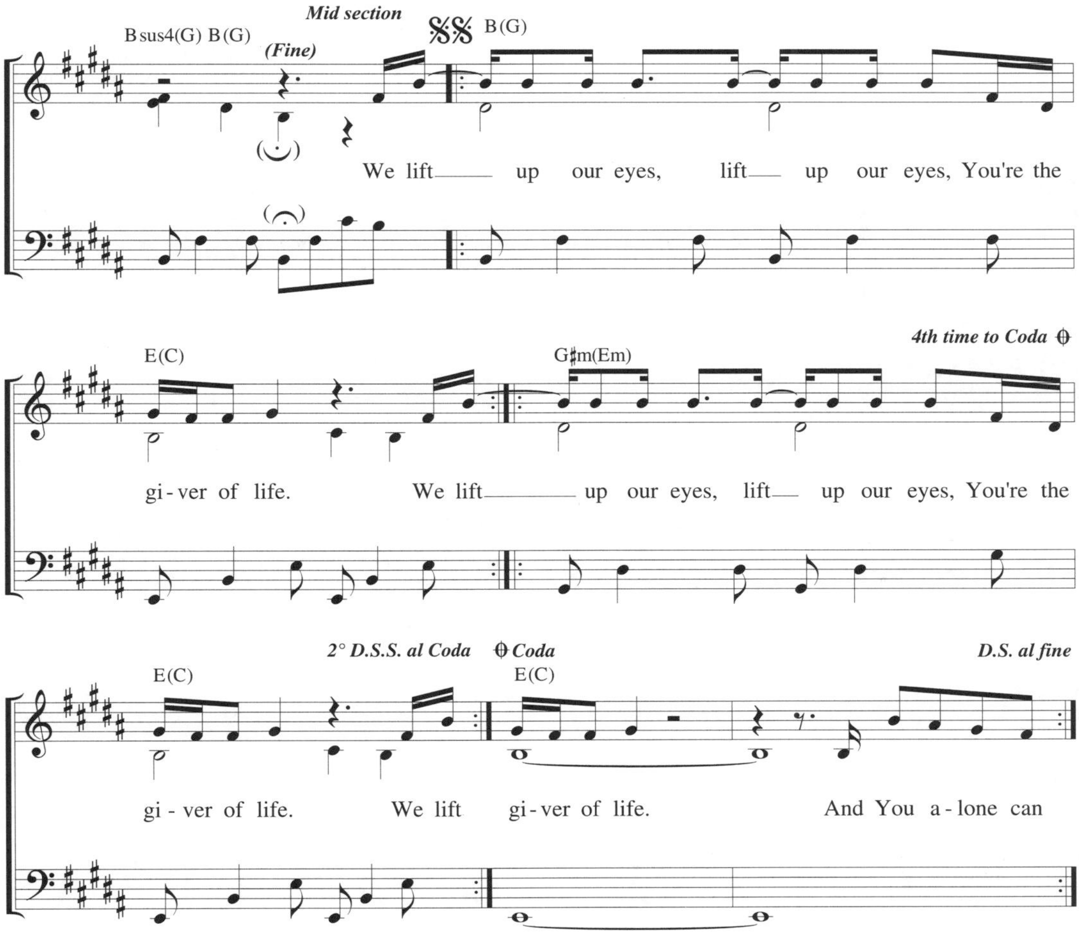

Mid section

Bsus4(G) B(G) *(Fine)* 𝄋𝄋 B(G)

We lift___ up our eyes, lift___ up our eyes, You're the

E(C) G♯m(Em) *4th time to Coda* ⊕

gi-ver of life. We lift___ up our eyes, lift___ up our eyes, You're the

2° D.S.S. al Coda ⊕ *Coda* *D.S. al fine*

E(C) E(C)

gi - ver of life. We lift gi-ver of life. And You a-lone can

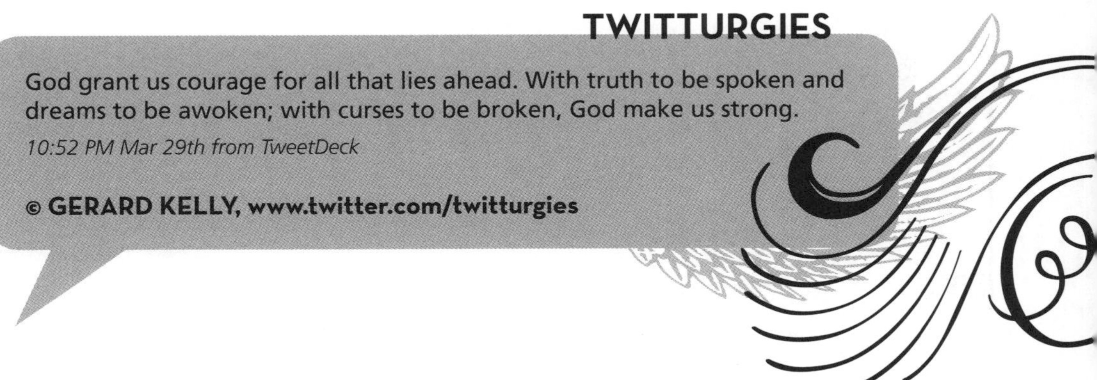

92. YOU ALONE ARE WORTHY

(Glory in the highest)

Capo 2(C)

Steady 4

Al Gordon, Luke Hellebronth
& Hanif Williams

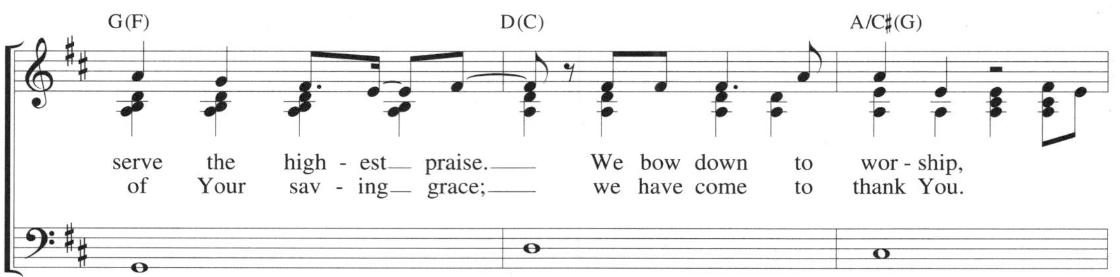

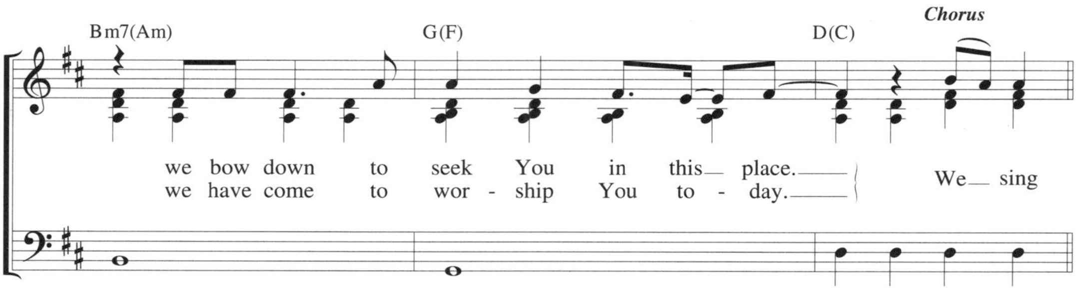

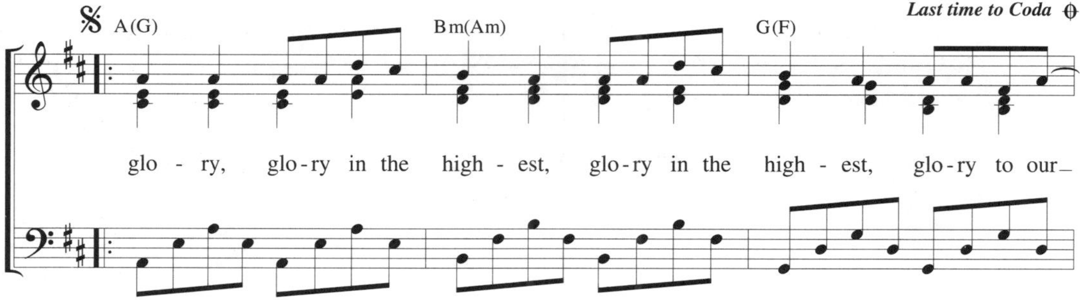

This song is recorded on the Spring Harvest 'Journey - Live Worship 2009' album

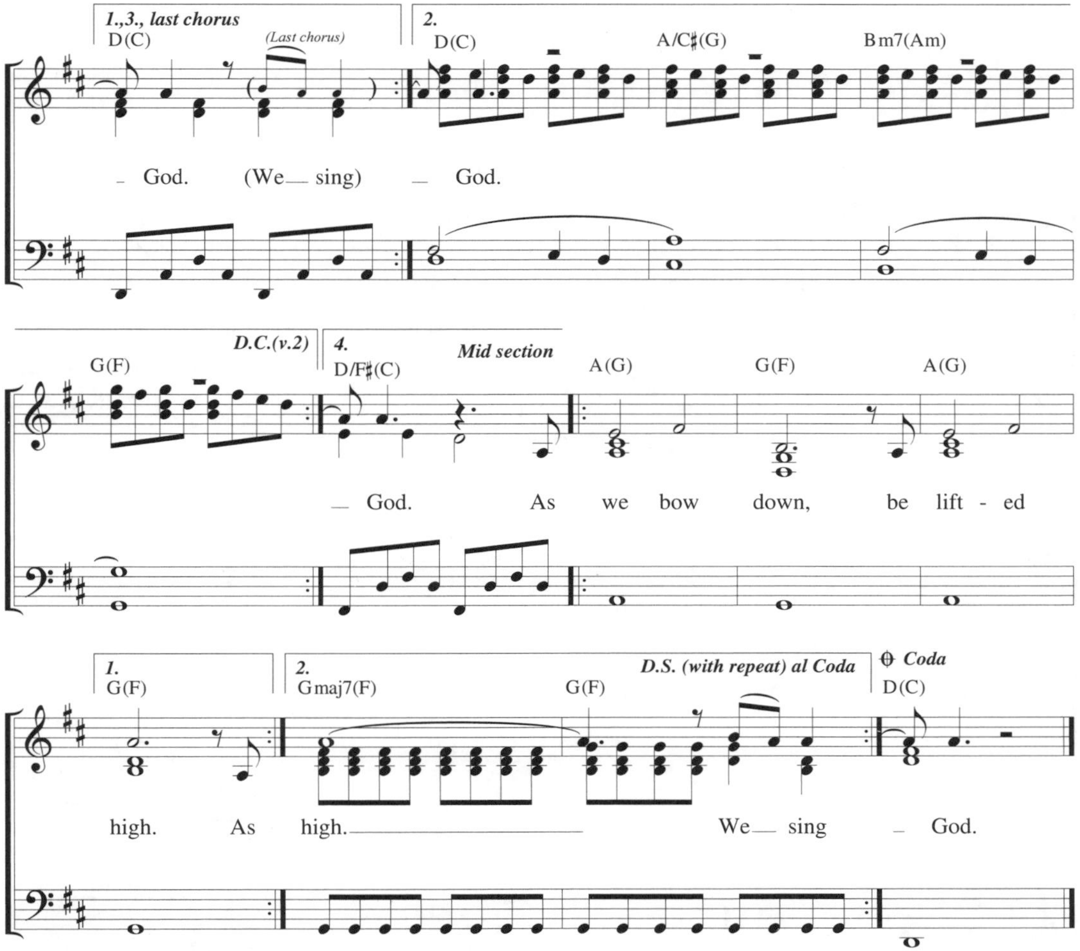

1.,3., last chorus — D(C) (*Last chorus*) | *2.* D(C) A/C♯(G) Bm7(Am)

– God. (We – sing) – God.

G(F) *D.C.(v.2)* | *4.* D/F♯(C) *Mid section* A(G) G(F) A(G)

– God. As we bow down, be lift - ed

1. G(F) | *2.* Gmaj7(F) G(F) *D.S. (with repeat) al Coda* | 𝄌 *Coda* D(C)

high. As high.______ We – sing – God.

93. YOU ARE MY STRENGTH

Reuben Morgan

G C2 D
1. D.C.(v.3)
You lift me up.
3. Un - fail - ing love
2. D.S.
3.
Mid section
C G
In the full-
Your love, O Lord,
D Em7 C G D Em7 C G
reach - es to the hea - vens,
Your faith - ful - ness
D Em7 C G
1. D Em7
2. D.C.
D
reach - es to the skies.
1. You are my

94. YOU ARE THE REASON
(God of all)

Ben Cantelon
& Robin Hardingham

Moderate rock

(v.2)
Em
D/F♯
Chorus
(small note last time)
Em
angels and pro - claim:
is the Lord of all'.
You are God of all
C G D Em
cre - a - tion, and the stars a - bove
C G D C
sing al - le - lu - ia, and to - ge - ther as
Last time to Coda
3rd time D.S. al Coda
Em Bm C D
one voice - we de - clare: You are
1.
D.C.(v.2)
Em C D/G Em/A
God. 2. You are for - e -

2.
(repeat 3 times)
Em
D
C
Em
D
C
God.
Mid section
C2
D
Glo - ry, glo - ry in the high - est.
C
D
Glo - ry, glo - ry in the high - est.
Em
D/F#
D.S.
Glo - ry, glo - ry in the high - est. You are
Coda
Cmaj7
D
Em
You are God.

YOU CAME TO SAVE THE WORLD 95.

(Third day)

Capo 3(D)

Simon Brading
& Matt Redman

C(A)
Bridge
Gm(Em)
Dm(Bm)
For three days,
You laid in that grave,
but
B♭(G)
C(A)
Chorus
death was swal-lowed up in vic-to-ry.
For You a-rose
F(D)
C(A)
Gm7(Em)
Last time to Coda
on the third day: 'Hal-le-lu-jah!' we cry, Your
on the third day; we are ful-ly a-live, in the
1.,3.,5.,6.,7.
B♭(G)
2.,4.
B♭(G)
life is our life.
(6.) (pow'r of Your life.)
Yes, You a-rose pow'r of Your life, You're a-live.
F/C (D)
1.
C(A)
B♭(G)

D.C.(v.2)
2.
Mid section
F(D)
C(A)
B♭(G)
You o-ver-came, You
o-ver-came at the cross. You
B♭(G)
Dm7(Bm)
rose a-gain, You rose a-gain, rais-ing us.
D.S. Coda
C(A)
B♭(G)
F/C (D)
For three days, pow'r of Your life, You're a-live.
C(A)
F(D)

96. YOU CAME TO US, THE SERVANT KING

(Great is our God)

Capo 1(G)

Cathy and Paul Burton
& Jim Elliot

With energy

B♭no3rd(A)
D♭(C)
Bridge
E♭(D)
What an awe - some God, what a-maz-
D♭(C)
E♭(D)
- ing love, and for e - ver we will sing.
Chorus
Fm7(Em)
A♭(G)
Great is our God, hal - le - lu - jah,
strong and migh - ty,
E♭(D)
B♭no3rd(A)
Fm7(Em)
great is our God, He will not fail, His love
King for e - ver more, He reigns
1.,3.,5.
2.
A♭(G)
E♭(D)
B♭no3rd(A)
E♭(D)
will ne - ver fail. Great is our God, more,
for e - ver

B♭no3rd(A)
Fm7(Em)
A♭(G)
E♭(D)
Yeah.
B♭no3rd(A)
D.C.
4.
E♭(D)
B♭no3rd(A)
D.S.
6.
E♭(D)
more,
more,
B♭no3rd(A)
Fm7(Em)
E♭(D)
Great is our God.
B♭sus2/D (A)
1.
D♭6(C)
2.
D♭maj7(C)
Great is our God.

YOU PAINT THE NIGHT

(God, You reign)

Lincoln Brewster
& Mia Fieldes

Moderate rock

G/D
Bm
(small notes 2°)
G
when to bring a new day; cre - a - tion sings: God, You reign.
and You call me by name; I live to say: God, You reign.
D
Chorus
G
God You reign, God You
(small notes 2° onwards)
Bm
A7sus4
G
Last time rit.
reign, for - e - ver and e - ver, God You
1., last time
D.C. (v.2)
2.,4.
D.S.
D
D
reign. reign. Whoa, God You
3.
D
Mid section
A/C♯
Em
D
Bm
A/C♯
reign. Hal - le - lu - jah, hal - le -

D A/C♯ Em D Bm A D A/C♯ G/B D/A
lu. Hal - le - lu - jah, hal - le - lu. Hal - le - lu - jah,
G A D A/C♯ G/B D/A Em7 A D
D.S. (with repeats) al Fine
hal - le - lu. Hal - le - lu - jah, hal - le - lu. God You

98. YOU FIND ME WITH ONE GLANCE

(Glorious life)

Lyrics: Nigel Briggs
Music: Trent

Moderately

This song is recorded on the Spring Harvest 'Glory - New Songs 2010' album

Em
G
D
Chorus
sings Your praise.
Through grace You've gi-ven li-ber-ty.
Asus4
Bm
Your mer-cy flow-ing o-ver me from dark-ness in-to glo-
G
D
Asus4
-ri-ous life.
Your hand has come to res-cue me and showed me
Bm
G
who I'm meant to be; in Je-sus there is glo-ri-ous life.
1st time D.C.
2nd time D.S.
Bm
D
G
Bm
2. You're

99. YOU SEE ALL THINGS

(Love divine)

Lyrics: Nigel Briggs
Music: Trent

Chorus
F♯/A♯
Bm
A
Oh, You are a love di - vine;
F♯m
there's no-thing bet - ter in this world that
G
Em
Bm
we could e - ver find. Oh, Your
A
F♯m
truth gives life; You came to set the cap -
G
Em
Last time to Coda
tives free and You've o - pened up our eyes.

1.
Bm
A/B
G
F♯sus4/C♯
F♯/A♯
D.C.
2.
Mid section
G
We were lost, now we're found, changed in - side and out when Your love came down.
A
G
A
Bm
D.S. al Coda
A2
G
F♯
F♯/A♯

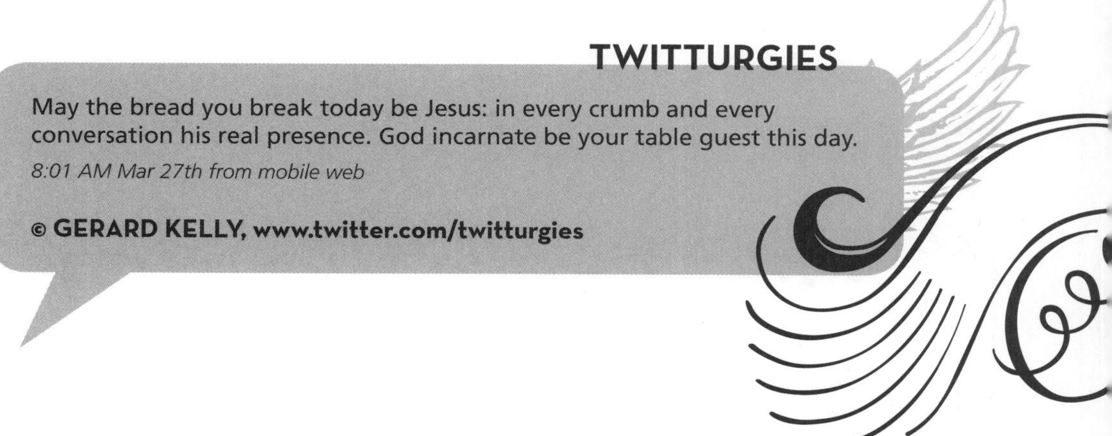

TWITTURGIES

May the bread you break today be Jesus: in every crumb and every conversation his real presence. God incarnate be your table guest this day.

8:01 AM Mar 27th from mobile web

100. YOUR GRACE IS ENOUGH

(This is our God)

Capo 4(C)

Reuben Morgan

This song is recorded on the Spring Harvest 'Glory - New Songs 2010' album

3.
Jump to S.S. al fine
1.,2.
(1st time D.C. v.2)
E(C)
Free - ly You gave
B(G)
F♯m(Dm)
C♯m(Am)
A(F)
E(C)
Mid section
E(C)
Free - ly You gave it all for us. Sur - ren - dered Your life
from death to life. For - ev - er our God
B(G)
1.
F♯m(Dm)
u - pon that cross. Great is the love poured out for all.
is glo - ri - fied. Ser - vant and King
C♯m(Am)
A(F)
E(C)
This is our God. Lift - ed on high

TWITTURGIES

God reign in me. Rain on me. Where you need to, reign me in. And where the song you hear from me wears thin, let your reign, in me, begin.

9:54 AM Mar 22nd from mobile web

ALL BECAUSE OF YOU 1.

David Ostby

```
Verse:
D
All because of You, I live and breathe
            Bm7
Every day;
       G                    D
I'm giving You the praise.

All because of You, I see and feel
            Bm7
Every day;
       G                  D
I'm giving You the fame.

Bridge:
                    G
You make me sing, sing, sing, sing.

     Chorus:
      D                        A
     I am because You are,
      F♯m7                     Gmaj7
     I live because You live,
       D                       A           F♯m7   Gmaj7   1. 3. [D   3. D/F♯ ]
     I love because You loved me first.

Mid section:
Bm7                A
I'm alive cos You're alive,
F♯m7               G2
I'm alive cos You're alive,
Bm7                 A              F♯m7   G2
I'm alive cos You're alive in me.  (Repeat)

G   A/G   Bm/G   A/G
                        Sing, . . .
```

2. A LIMITLESS MAJESTY

(You are greater)

Ben Jones
& Sue Rinaldi

Verse 1:
Gmaj7 A D
A limitless majesty,
Gmaj7
A depth beyond all that I see;
D Dsus4 D
Perfection in mystery.
Gmaj7 A D
A mind that created the soul,
Gmaj7
A love that is making me whole,
A D F♯7
Eternally faithful and true.

Chorus:
D Bm G
You are greater, You are higher, I see;
Gm D Dmaj7
Have all of me.
D Bm G
There's none more graceful, none more powerful than You;
Gm D [F♯7] [***Chorus repeat*** Dmaj7]
Take all of me.

Verse 2:
Gmaj7 A D
My life can never reflect
Gmaj7
The beauty of Your perfectness;
D Dsus4 D
Christ, live in me, for Your glory.
Gmaj7 A D
Trying to make it alone,
Gmaj7
Feels like I'm running from home;
A D F♯7
Lord, keep my path straight and true.

Tag:
Gmaj7 D
A heart that's dripping with grace,
Gmaj7
A Father that longs to embrace,
A D
Mercy that makes me complete.

This song is recorded on the Spring Harvest 'Glory - New Songs 2010' album

ALL I ONCE HELD DEAR

(Knowing You)

3.

Graham Kendrick

Verse 1:

```
C  G/B Am   F    C                   F   G  C
All I    once held dear, built my life upon,
    G/B Am  F  C             Am       G
All this world reveres, and wars to own,
C     F     G           C    C/E   F     G   Am/C
All I once thought gain I have counted loss;
         G/B Am  F    C            Am        Gsus4   G
Spent and worthless now, compared to this.
```

Chorus:

```
              F6    C     F/G
Knowing You, Jesus,
G             C              Am   Em/G   F
Knowing You, there is no greater thing.
               C/E                 F/A
You're my all, You're the best,
               C/G                 F
You're my joy, my righousness,
[Rpt.]  C/E         F/A   C/G   G
   And I love You, Lord.
[Last x] C/E       F/A    C/G   F/G        C
   And I love You, Lord,           love You, Lord.
```

Verse 2:

```
C    G/B Am       F  C         F       G    C
Now my heart's desire is to know You more,
   G/B Am  F  C           Am         G
To be found in You and known as Yours.
C        F    G  C    C/E     F      G   Am/C
To possess by faith what I could not earn,
     G/B Am   F    C        Am       Gsus4   G
All-sur - pas - sing gift of righteousness.
```

Verse 3:

```
C   G/B Am  F   C                    F  G  C
Oh, to know the power of Your risen life,
    G/B Am   F     C         Am     G
And to know You in Your sufferings.
C      F      G    C  C/E        F       C   Am/C
To become like You in Your death, my Lord,
     G/B Am  F C         Am    Gsus4    G
So with You to live and never die.
```

This song is recorded on the Spring Harvest 'Journey - Live Worship 2009' album

4. ALL THE HEAVENS PRAISE

(Great and glorious)

Capo 5;

Jo Petch

Verse 1:

```
Am                        F                           C          G
   All the heavens praise    Your wonderful ways,    O God.
Am                       F                            C          G
   Choirs of angels sing,    sing of all You've done,    O God.
```

Bridge:

```
Am                       F                            C          G
   Every knee will bow    to worship at Your throne,    O God.
Am                       F                  C                         G
   Every heart will cry:    'Holy is Your name,    holy is Your name'.
```

Chorus:

```
F                        C
Great and glorious,
            Em               Am
You reign,     You reign.
             F                  C                  G
All the heavens and the earth cry out in praise.
```

[**Repeat - but not 1st x**]

Verse 2:

```
Am                  F                            C          G
   Over all the earth    Your glory fills the skies,    O God.
Am                   F                           C          G
   High and lifted up,    and holy is Your name,    O God.
```

Mid section:

```
            F                G
There's no one higher, no one greater,
   F                G
No one is more powerful.
            F              G                          F/A   G
There's no one wiser, no one stronger than You.
            F                G
There's no one higher, no one greater,
   F                G
No one is more powerful.
           Dm              G                         F          G
There's no one wiser, no one stronger than You.   Our God.
```

Coda:

```
G                                Fmaj7
   There's no one like You, God.
```

[**Repeat x5**]

This song is recorded on the Spring Harvest 'Glory - New Songs 2010' album

ALL THE ROOM WAS HUSHED AND STILL 5.

(Love each other)

<u>**Capo 3(G)**</u>

Graham Kendrick

Intro:

```
Am/C   Em   D/A   Am/C   Em   D/A   D
```

Verse 1:

```
          Am        Em          D/F#   D
All the room was hushed and still,
      C          G/D       D/F#   D
And when the bowl was filled
    Am          Em          D/F#   D
He stooped to wash their feet.
      C        G/D      D/F#   D
And when it was complete,        he said:
G                                 D/F#
   'This is what I'm asking you to do,
Em                                       Gsus4 G   D
   This is why I'm kneeling here beside    you.'
G                               D/F#
   'This is what I want my church to be,
Em                  D                    C  C2
   This is what I want the world to see who it is you follow.'
```

Chorus:

```
G                       D/F#
   'Love each other,        one another,
Em                          C2
   Love each other in the way that I have loved you.'
G                    D/F#
   'Walk together,       and whatever comes,
Em                          C                            [C2   Am/C   Em   D]
   Love each other in the way that I have loved you.'
```

Verse 2:

```
          Am     Em            D/F#   D
Let the room be hushed and still,
        C      G/D      D/F#   D
Let us go to where he kneels
      Am      Em   D/F#   D
And join him as he serves,
     C        G/D      D/F#   D
And learn his ways of love,
G                                 D/F#
   'This is what I'm asking you to do,
Em                                       Gsus4 G   D
   This is why I'm kneeling here beside    you.'
G                               D/F#
   'This is what I want my church to be,
Em                  D                    C  C2
   This is what I want the world to see who it is you follow.'
```

This song is recorded on the Spring Harvest 'Journey - Live Worship 2009' album

6. AS WE COME INTO YOUR PRESENCE

(Because of Your love)

Paul Baloche
Brenton Brown

Verse:

```
         G/B     C2          Dsus4  G
As we come into Your   presence,
        G/B       C2     Dsus4 G
We remember every  blessing
                  G/B     C2      Dsus4 G/B          C2
That You've poured out so freely from above.
          G/B  C2          Dsus4  G
Lifting gratitude and    praises
          G/B       C2  Dsus4  G
For compassion so   amazing,
                G/B        C2           Dsus4    G/B                  C2
Lord, we've come to give You thanks for all You've done.
```

Chorus:

```
                          G/B   C2    Dsus4
Because of Your love
               G/B   C2    Dsus4
We're forgiven,
                          G/B   C2    Dsus4
Because of Your love
                          G/B   C2    Dsus4
Our hearts are clean.
                   G/B   C2    Dsus4
We lift You up
                       G/B   C2    Dsus4
With songs of freedom,
    A7/C♯  C2
Forever we're changed
D                    G(no3rd)
   Because of Your love.
G/B   C2    Dsus4    G    G/B   C2    Dsus4    G
   Yeah,                         yeah.
```

AT THE CROSS, WHERE JESUS SUFFERED

7.

(Merciful)

Graham Kendrick

Verse 1:

```
        D                    A/C♯  D
At the cross, where Jesus suf  -  fered,
               G/B  A
I lay down my bitter blame;
           Bm          Em7 D/F♯ A    Bm
Where he prayed: "Father, for - give them",
        Bm                  A      D
Lord, I know that I must do the same.
                                A
Laying down my pain, my anger,
           D               A     G
Vengeful thoughts nailed to the cross;
        D                 G                    Em          Em/A  D
Take the sting of wrongs remembered, no more measuring my      loss.
```

Chorus:

```
        G          F♯m      D         G      Bm A
For my Father in heaven showed mercy to me.
D/F♯    G    D/F♯  G  A  Bm                  Em       Em/A Bm
How can I not be   merciful when God's been merciful to      me,
             Em        Em/A   D   [Dsus4   D] [Last x Em/A    D]
God's been merciful to         me. me.
```

Verse 2:

```
        D                    A/C♯  D
I'll not use my words as wea  -  pons
               G/B      A
Or the past to gain control;
         Bm         Em7 D/F♯ A  Bm
On my tongue no trace   of   venom,
       Bm                A          D
Only grace to comfort and make whole.
                               A
I am weak, but God is with me,
          D      A      G
Past and future in his hand –
          D                G                 Em          Em/A  D
Turns to good the ill we suffer, works all things into Love's plan.
```

Verse 3:

```
      D                   A/C♯ D
Holy Dove, return and rest here,
               G/B       A
As I think and speak the best;
           Bm       Em7 D/F♯ A    Bm
Though it takes ten thousand choices
          Bm           A       D
I'll press on to honour and to bless.
                                 A
For the love of Christ my Saviour,
         D          A     G
By the strength he daily gives;
          D                G              Em     Em/A   D
This will be the thanks I offer: I will totally for  -  give.
```

8. BE LIFTED HIGH ABOVE THE HEAVENS

(Ring out)

Tim Sanders

Verse:

```
   A
Be lifted high above the heavens,
A/C♯                          D                  A
Let Your greatness shine above the earth, O God.

We're gathered to make known Your worth,
F♯m7                         Esus4
Singing to the tune of Your glory.
         Bm            A/C♯
Joined in unity, with one harmony;
     D                                        A
We rejoice in You our God for Your love endures.
```

Bridge:

```
   D              A        E   A/C♯
Together with one heart we bring,
  D         A       E
United as one voice we'll sing
```

Chorus:

```
     A/C♯   D2
Your praise.
      A                  E
Every tongue will confess:
             A/C♯   D2
"You're great,
     A           E
And greatly to be praised".
       A/C♯          D2
One God,      one King,
       A           E              A/C♯   D2   Esus4
Let the universe ring out Your name.
```

Mid section:

```
A                               D
Glory, honour, praise and power    be to our God forever.
F♯m                             D
Glory, honour, praise and power    be to our God forever.
A                               D
Glory, honour, praise and power    be to our God forever.
F♯m                             D                       A  D
Glory, honour, praise and power    be to our God forever.
       F♯m   D        A   D       F♯m   D  A
Forever.        Forever.       Forever.  [To Bridge]
```

Coda:

```
       A           E        A/C♯         D2
Let the universe ring out One God, one King,
       A           E        A/C♯         D2
Let the universe ring out One God, one King,
       A           E              A/C♯     D2     Esus4
Let the universe ring out Your name.
```

BEFORE THE WORLD WAS MADE 9.

(Glory to God forever)

Steve Fee
& Vicky Beeching

Capo 4

Verse 1:
G/B C2 G D
Before the world was made, before You spoke it to us,
G/B C2 G D
You were the King of kings, yeah, You were, yeah, You were.
G/B C2 G D
And now You're reigning still, enthroned above all things;
G/B C2 G D
Angels and saints cry out, we join them as we sing.

Chorus:
C G D Em
Glory to God, glory to God,
C G D
Glory to God forever.
C G D Em
Glory to God, glory to God,
C G D C G D Em C G D
Glory to God forever. Yeah.

Verse 2:
G/B C2 G D
Creator God, You gave me breath so I could praise
G/B C2 G D
Your great and matchless name all my days, all my days.
G/B C2 G D
So let my whole life be a blazing offering,
G/B C2 G D
A life that shouts and sings the greatness of our King.

Mid section:
C G
Take my life and let it be
D Em
All for You and for Your glory,
C G D
Take my life and let it be Yours.

This song is recorded on the Spring Harvest 'Glory - New Songs 2010' album

10. BEHOLD, A BROKEN WORLD

Words: Timothy DudleySmith from Micah 4
Music trad. arr. David Peacock

Verse 1:

```
   Em     D/E    Em          Am/E
Behold a broken world, we pray,
        Em7       Am/E  Bm7/E
Where want and war increase,
      Em         D/F#      G        Am
And grant us, Lord, in this our day,
     C/B     Bm7       Em
The ancient dream of peace.
   G                     Am/G  G
A dream of sword to sickles bent,
    Am9       Bm          C2    D
Of spears to scythe and spade,
      Em        D/F#    G         Am/C
The weapons of our warfare spent,
  C/B       Bm       Em  D/E     Em  D/E     Em  D/E     Em
A world of peace remade.
```

Verse 2:

```
Bm7   Em     D/E    Em     Am/E
Where every battle flag is furled
      Em7   Am/E    Bm7/E
And every trumpet stilled,
        Em           D/F#     G        Am
Where wars shall cease in all the world,
  C/B      Bm7         Em
A waking dream fulfilled.
    G                       Am/G    G
No force of arms shall there prevail
     Am9    Bm         C2    D
Nor justice cease her sway;
      Em          D/F#    G         Am/C
Nor shall their loftiest visions fail
     C/B       Bm     Em  D/E     Em  D/E     Em  D/E     Em
The dreamers of the day.
```

Verse 3:

```
Bm7  Em        D/E           Em      Am/E
O    Prince of peace, who died to save,
  Em7        Am/E  Bm7/E
A lost world to redeem,
     Em     D/F#        G          Am
And rose in triumph from the grave,
    C/B       Bm7      Em
Behold our waking dream.
        G                      Am/G  G
Bring, Lord, Your better world to birth,
      Am9        Bm        C2    D
Your kingdom, love's domain;
         Em          D/F#       G          Am/C
Where peace with God, and peace on earth,
      C/B      Bm    Em
And peace eternal reign.
```

BREATHE ON ME

E. Hatch adpt. Darren Baird

Capo 3

Verse 1:

              G2   D2/F♯
Breathe on me, Breath of God,
                G2   D2/F♯
Fill me with life a new,
               G2   D2/F♯
That I may love what Thou dost love,
                G2   D2/F♯
And do as Thou would do.
               G2   D/F♯
Breathe on me, Breath of God
            Em Bm/D A/C♯
Until my heart   is   pure,
     D   G2   Bm7
Until my will is one with Thine,
             Em D/F♯ A/C♯
To do and to   en - dure;
D   G2   G2/A   D
Breathe on me,   Breath of God.

Verse 2:

              G2   D2/F♯
Breathe on me, Breath of God,
              G2   D2/F♯
Till I am wholly thine,
               G2   D2/F♯
Till all this earthly part of me
                    G2   D2/F♯
Glows with thy fire divine.
               G2   D/F♯
Breathe on me, Breath of God,
            Em Bm/D A/C♯
So shall I ne - ver   die,
      D   G2   Bm7
But live with Thee the perfect life
             Em D/F♯ A/C♯
Of Thine eter - ni - ty;
D   G2   G2/A   D
Breathe on me,   Breath of God.

12. BREAK OUR HEARTS

Vicky Beeching

Capo 3

Chorus:

```
D                          A/C♯
Break our hearts with the things that break Yours,
Bm              G
Wake us up to see through Your eyes.
D                          A/C♯
Break our hearts with the things that break Yours,
    Bm              G                 D   [A   Bm   G]
And send us out to shine in the darkness.
```

Verse 1:

```
   Bm            A/C♯                D
It's time for us to live the songs we sing,
    Bm              A         G
And turn our good intentions into actions;
   Bm                A/C♯         D
To bring the kind of worship You desire,
    Bm                 A               G
And move beyond our self-absorbed distractions.
```

Bridge:

```
    Em          Bm         A
The mountains are shaking,
          Em          Bm  A
Could this be a great awakening?
```

Verse 2:

```
   Bm                A/C♯               D
It's time to move outside our comfort zones,
   Bm                 A          G
To see beyond our churches and our homes;
   Bm                  A/C♯                D
To change the way we think and how we spend,
   Bm             A        G
Until we look like Jesus again.
```

Coda:

```
A               Bm              G               D
  We will shine,    we will shine, we will shine,
A                Bm   G   D
  We will shine.
```

BY THIS WORLD MY HEART WAS WOUNDED 13.

(Sweet Jesus)

Brian Houston

Capo 4

Verse 1:

```
G              G/B C              G
By this world my  heart was wounded,
Em      Bm       A   A7  D7
Yet by love my soul was healed.
G               G/B C             G
Mercy soothed my  pain and longing,
Em          Bm       G/D  E        G
Truth and grace in Love revealed.
```

Chorus:

```
E           G            C          E          G
Jesus, sweet Jesus, Your praise my soul must sing.
E           G          C          D7         G
Jesus, sweet Jesus, my hope, my light, my King.
```

Verse 2:

```
 G        G/B C             G
I was lost and darkness held me,
Em     Bm     A    A7  D7
Every day I stumbled on.
G              G/B C               G
Then the light of    Love o'ercame me,
Em            Bm       G/D  E        G
Whispering:'Sinner, come on home'.
```

Verse 3:

```
 G             G/B C             G
Suffering, still my close companion;
Em       Bm       A  A7 D7
Pain, no stranger on my way.
G           G/B   C              G
Yet, redemption's purpose fashions
Em       Bm   G/D  E   G
Wisdom and humi  -  lity.
```

This song is recorded on the Spring Harvest 'Glory - New Songs 2010' album

14. BY FAITH WE SEE THE HAND OF GOD

Keith and Kristyn Getty
& Stuart Townend

Verse 1:
Ano3rd D/A Ano3rd Amaj7 D/A
By faith, we see the hand of God
Ano3rd D/F♯ Esus4
In the light of creation's grand design;
A2/C♯ D2 D2/F♯ E/G♯ A F♯m7 E D2 Esus4 F♯m
In the lives of those who prove his faithful - ness,
D E Ano3rd Amaj7 D/A
Who walk by faith and not by sight.

Verse 2:
Ano3rd D/A Ano3rd Amaj7 D/A
By faith, our fathers roamed the earth
Ano3rd D/F♯ Esus4
With the pow'r of his promise in their hearts:
A2/C♯ D2 D2/F♯ E/G♯ A F♯m7 E D2 Esus4 F♯m
Of a ho - ly ci - ty built by God's own hand–
D E Ano3rd
A place where peace and justice reign.

Chorus:
A F♯m D2 A
We will stand as children of the promise,
F♯m D2 A E
We will fix our eyes on him: our soul's reward.
A F♯m D2 A A2/C♯ D2
Till the race is finished and the work is done,
Bm7 D E [**1.2.** Asus2 D/A Asus4 D/A] [**3.** A]
We'll walk by faith and not by sight.

Verse 3:
Ano3rd D/A Ano3rd Amaj7 D/A
By faith, the prophets saw a day
Ano3rd D/F♯ Esus4
When the longed for Messiah would appear
A2/C♯ D2 D2/F♯ E/G♯ A F♯m7 E D2 Esus4 F♯m
With the pow'r to break the chains of sin and death,
D E Ano3rd Amaj7 D/A
And rise triumphant from the grave.

Verse 4:
Ano3rd D/A Ano3rd Amaj7 D/A
By faith, the church was called to go
Ano3rd D/F♯ Esus4
In the power of the Spirit to the lost
A2/C♯ D2 D2/F♯ E/G♯ A F♯m7 E D2 Esus4 F♯m
To deli - ver cap - tives and to preach good news
D E Ano3rd
In every corner of the earth.

Verse 5:
Ano3rd D/A Ano3rd Amaj7 D/A
By faith, this mountain shall be moved,
Ano3rd D/F♯ Esus4
And the power of the gospel shall prevail,
A2/C♯ D2 D2/F♯ E/G♯ A F♯m7 E D2 Esus4 F♯m
For we know in Christ all things are pos - si - ble
D E Ano3rd
For all who call upon his name.

CAN YOU HEAR, THERE'S A NEW SONG 15.

(A new hallelujah)

Michael W. Smith, Paul Baloche
& Debbie Smith

Verse 1:

```
      G                C/G  G
Can you hear, there's a new song,
                                 C/G G
Breaking out from the children of freedom.
                         C/G G
Every race and every nation,
                              C/G G   G(no3rd)   C/G   G  C(no3rd)   C/G   G
Sing it out, sing a new hallelujah.
```

Verse 2:

```
     G                C/G G
Let us sing love to the nations,
                                  C/G  G
Bringing hope of the grace that has freed us.
                              C/G G
Make it known, and make him famous;
                              C/G G   G(no3rd)   C/G   G  C(no3rd)   C/G   G
Sing it out, sing a new hallelujah.
```

Chorus:

```
     C                         G
Arise,      let the church arise;
        C                         G
Let love      reach to the other side.
      Em                C
Alive,       come alive,
                  G(no3rd)   C/G   G   G(no3rd)   C/G   G
Let the song arise.
```

Coda:

```
                           C/G G                          C/G G
Every one sing a new hallelujah; everyone sing a new hallelujah.
```

Verse 3:

```
     G               C/G  G
All the world sings a new song,
                               C/G G
Reaching out with a new hallelujah.
                       C/G   G
Every son and every daughter,
                             C/G G   G(no3rd)   C/G   G  C(no3rd)   C/G   G
Every one sing a new hallelujah.
```

Mid section:

```
F    Am      G
Oh, (oh,) yeah. (yeah.)
      F                  Am             G
Let the song arise, (let the song arise,) yeah. (yeah.)
       F                 Am          G   C/G   G   C/G   G
Let the song arise, (let the song arise.)
```

16. COME, LEARN OF GOD'S KINGDOM

Words: Timothy DudleySmith
Music: English folk tune arr. Richard Hubbard

Intro: G F/G C/G G

Verse 1:

```
        G              C/G           Am/G       D/G
Come, learn of God's kingdom, the kingdom of light,
  G          Am7       Bm7      Am7  G
Its dawning dispelling the darkness of    night;
                   Bm7      Cmaj7   D
The light of God's glory is shining abroad,
  G             C/G           D/G C/G  G     F/G   C/G   G
In splendour proclaiming that Jesus is    Lord.
```

Verse 2:

```
        G              C/G           Am/G       D/G
Come, seek for God's kingdom, the kingdom of Christ,
  G                 Am7    Bm7     Am7 G
A pearl without equal, a treasure unpriced,
          Bm7        Cmaj7       D
A city unshaken the years cannot move,
        G      C/G      D/G    C/G G    F/G   C/G   G
Where life everlasting is founded on love.
```

Verse 3:

```
        G           C/G            Am/G          D/G
Come, enter God's kingdom, the gates are flung wide;
  G            Am7        Bm7     Am7  G
To win us our freedom the Saviour has   died:
                 Bm7          Cmaj7         D
The keys of the kingdom are theirs who proclaim
    G          C/G        D/G    C/G G    F/G   C/G   G
The word of the gospel and faith in his   Name.
```

Verse 4:

```
  G         C/G          Am/G  D/G
Inherit God's kingdom; for Jesus declares
  G             Am7          Bm7      Am7  G
To those who confess him, the kingdom is      theirs:
                Bm7        Cmaj7    D
O come then rejoicing his glories to sing,
  G           C/G              D/G     C/G G    F/G   C/G   D/G   C/G   G
As heirs of that kingdom where Christ is the King.
```

COME, SEE THE SON

17.

Capo 3

Joel Payne

Verse 1:

```
G                              D  G      Em
Come, see the Son of the living God, hanging on a tree,
Dsus4             D            G   Em   D/F♯
Dying there for you and me.
G                                  D   G      Em
Come, see the bringer of truth and grace, nailed there for us;
Dsus4   D                G
Agony across his face.
```

Chorus 1 & 2:

```
          C              C2
This is love displayed,
C         G/B       Em7                     C    D
This is mercy perfectly portrayed in Christ,
                     G   Em7   D/F♯  G   Em7   D/F♯   G
The cross of Christ.
```

Verse 2:

```
G                              D  G      Em
Come, see the innocent Son of God, punished there for us,
Dsus4             D            G   Em   D/F♯
Rescuing us with his blood.
G                                  D   G      Em
Come, see the healer of wounded souls, crucified for us;
Dsus4   D                G
Broken there to make us whole.
```

Verse 3:

```
G                                        D  G          Em
Come, see the tomb where they laid him down, the stone is rolled away;
Dsus4              D                     G   Em   D/F♯
Nothing but the grave clothes now.
G                               D G  Em
Come, see the King is alive again, risen from the dead,
Dsus4      D          G
Ushering a new age in.
```

Chorus 3:

```
          C     C2
This is victory,
C         G/B       Em7                     C    D
This is life for everyone who will believe
                 G
In Jesus Christ.    [Repeat]
```

Tag:

```
G               C                      G/B        Em7
Come and worship him, come and sing to him,
              C          D            G
Come and live for him,    Jesus Christ.  [Repeat]
```

18. CREATION SINGS THE FATHER'S SONG

Keith and Kristyn Getty
& Stuart Townend

Verse 1:

```
    C    G/C       F/C      C  G/C       F/C        C        F      G   Am
Creation sings the Father's song;    He calls the sun to wake the dawn
      F                   C/E        F          C/E      G          C    G/C    F/C    C    G/C    F/C
And run the course of day,  till evening falls in crimson rays.
     C     G/C       F/C       C  G/C       F/C        C           F   G     Am
His fingerprints in flakes of snow,  His breath upon this spinning globe;
    F                     C/E           F            C/E        G      C
He charts the eagle's flight,  commands the newborn baby's cry.
```

Chorus:

```
    G   Am
Hallelujah!
     F      C/E   G            C            G    Am
Let all creation stand and sing: 'Hallelujah!'
          F      C/E              F   C/E
Fill the earth with songs of worship,
           F          C/E  G       [ C     G/C    F/C  x3]   C    [G/C    F/C]
Tell the wonders of creation's King.
```

Verse 2:

```
   C       G/C      F/C      C  G/C       F/C       C        F         G    Am
Creation gazed upon His face;     the Ageless One in time's embrace,
    F                       C/E      F        C/E    G           C    G/C    F/C   C    G/C    F/C
Unveiled the Father's plan of reconciling God and man.
  C        G/C   F/C           C  G/C        F/C          C              F       G   Am
A second Adam walked the earth, whose blameless life would break the curse,
         F                        C/E    F          C/E    G      C
Whose death would set us free to live with him eternally.
```

Verse 3:

```
    C     G/C       F/C   C  G/C      F/C            C          F   G   Am
Creation longs for his return, when Christ shall reign upon the earth;
     F                C/E        F             C/E G          C    G/C    F/C    C    G/C    F/C
The bitter wars that rage are birth pains of a coming age.
        C    G/C       F/C        C  G/C     F/C             C           F      G Am
When He renews the land and sky,      all heav'n will sing and earth reply
     F                     C/E             F      C/E    G           C
With one resplendent theme: the glory of our God and King!
```

DEFENDER OF THIS HEART 19.

(Remain)

Ben Cantelon

Verse 1:

D   A
   Defender of this heart,
                                  Bm
You loved me from the start,
           G
You never change.
D   A
   Through the highs and lows,
                              Bm
As seasons come and go,
          G
You never fail.

Bridge:

G   D
Day after day
      A   Bm
Your love will remain
G   D
Faithful and true,
               A
You are good.

Chorus:

          G   D/F♯   A
You are God with us, You're victorious,
D/F♯   G   D/F♯   A
You are strong and mighty to save.
               G   D/F♯   A
For Your word stands true, there is none like You,
D/F♯   G   D/F♯   A
And when all else fades You remain.

Em   G   D   A
Em   G   D   A   [D]

Verse 2:

D   A
   When troubles come my way,
                              Bm
You guide and You sustain;
          G
Lead me, I pray.
D   A
   Forever You will be
                           Bm
The great eternal King,
          G
Now and always.

20. DARK BEFORE THE DAWN

(His love)

<u>**Capo 3**</u>

Phil Barlow, Steve Barlow
& Ray Goudie

Verse 1:

```
G                     C/G      D/F♯              C/G  G
Dark before the dawn,    the Father's heart is broken;
Em7          G/B      C              D
Watching while his only Son is beaten shamefully.
G                     C/G    D/F♯              C/G  G
Here I stand amazed,     he drank the cup of suffering,
Em7                 C              G/D        D
Laying down his own life to die in agony.
G/B                C        G/D              Em
What a great surrender, what a great surrender,
G/D                C            Am7              Dsus4    D
What a great surrender: he gave his life for me.
```

Chorus:

```
    G                         C                   G/B      C      Dsus4    D
His love has more than conquered, his love has paid for me.
B/D♯ Em   Em/D              A/C♯
The price          that was demanded:
[1.2.4.]
    G/D                    Dsus4   D      Gsus4    G    C2    Cmaj7  [Last x G]
Oh, my Saviour, why so much        for me?
[3.]
G/D                      D
Oh, my Saviour, why so much for me?
```

Verse 2:

```
G                        C/G  D/F♯             C/G  G
There upon the cross,     I see the plan unfolded;
Em7        G/B   C              D
Why the One so lovely was crucified for me.
G                        C/G      D/F♯              C/G  G
Even through the pain     he offered such forgiveness;
Em7              C                 G/D                     D
All he did was love us, and how did we repay?
G/B                C        G/D              Em
We are now forgiven, we are now forgiven,
G/D               C              Am7              Dsus4    D
We are now forgiven, and this is now our claim:
```

Verse 3:

```
G                        C/G   D/F♯              C/G  G
What a great exchange,     grace so freely given!
    Em7       G/B       C          D
Redemption bells are ringing: Christ has won it all!
G                           C/G         D/F♯                  C/G  G
Now the dawn has come,      there's hope for each new morning;
Em7          C        G/D                 D
All creation singing songs of liberty.
G/B                C          G/D                  Em
He cried: 'It is finished', my heart sings: 'It's finished',
G/D                C               Am7                Dsus4    D
Once for all it's finished, all heaven and earth agree.
```

This song is recorded on the Spring Harvest 'Glory - New Songs 2010' album

DELIVERERER, COME SET ME FREE 21.

(Deliverer)

Vicky Beeching
& Sarah MacIntosh

Verse 1:

```
           Am                  F
Deliverer, come set me free,
                  C              G/B
Break every chain holding me.
           Am                   F
Deliverer, come have Your way;
            C                G/B
I surrender to Your rule and reign.
```

Chorus:

```
                Fmaj7 Am      C          G/B
Where the Spirit   of   the Lord is, there is freedom.
                Fmaj7 Am       C        G/B
Where the Spirit   of   the Lord is, there is healing.
```

Verse 2:

```
                    Am                          F
You say the word and mountains are moved,
                  C                    G/B
Oceans and stars stand in awe of You.
                    Am                  F
Just say the word, I will be changed;
                     C                            G/B
We'll see Your face and we will not be the same.
```

Middle section:

```
              Dm                     Am     G
Where the Spirit of the Lord is, there is freedom.
              Dm                     Am     G
Where the Spirit of the Lord is, there is hope.
              Dm                     Am     G       F
Where the Spirit of the Lord is, there is healing.

              Dm7                         Am    G
And Your blood is enough to break every chain. [Repeat x8]
```

And where the . . .

This song is recorded on the Spring Harvest 'Glory - New Songs 2010' album

22. EVERLASTING GOD

(Yesterday, today and forever)

Vicky Beeching

<u>Capo 3</u>

Verse 1:

```
G                    Bm7
Everlasting God,
      G                        Bm7
The years go by but You're unchanging.
G                        Bm7
In this fragile world,
       G                Bm7
You are the only firm foundation.
Em7add4                              D/F#
           Always loving, always true,
G                                         Bm7              A
           Always merciful and good,       so good.
```

Chorus:

```
      D/F#       G       Bm7       A
      Yesterday, today and forever,
      D/F#              G            Bm7                  A
      You are the same,  You never change.
      D/F#       G       Bm7       A
      Yesterday, today and forever,
      Em7                        G          A               [D/F#  G  Bm7  A]  [Last x D]
      You are faithful and we will trust in You.
```

Verse 2:

```
G                  Bm7
Uncreated One,
      G                      Bm7
You have no end and no beginning.
G                        Bm7
Earthly powers fade,
      G                      Bm7
But there is no end to Your kingdom.
Em7add4                               D/F#
           Always loving, always true,
G                                         Bm7              A
           Always merciful and good,       so good.
```

Chorus

```
      D/F#       G       Bm7       A
      Yesterday, today and forever,
      D/F#              G         Bm7               A
      You are the same,  You never change.
      D/F#       G       Bm7       A
      Yesterday, today and forever,
      Em7                        G          A             G
      You are faithful and we will trust in You.
                            D/F#                      G        D/F#
      We will trust in You, we will trust in You, in You.
```

Bridge:

```
G2          D/F#                    G2          D/F#
Yahweh, God unchanging. Yahweh, firm foundation. (x2) Chorus repeat:
```

This song is recorded on the Spring Harvest 'One Hope - Live worship 2008' and 'Kids Praise Party 3' albums

FOREVER AND A DAY

Ben Jones

Verse :

```
A                      D2                            Bm
   Forever and a day, I will give You praise
                          E
For all You are and all You have,
                          F♯m   E/G♯    A   D   A/C♯
I will give You praise.
A                      D2                            Bm
   Forever and a day, I will love Your name,
                                E
For all You've done and yet to do,
                           F♯m   E/G♯    A
I will love Your name.
                  D2                      E2
Forever and a day, I will give You praise.
```

Chorus:

```
A              F♯m7                    D2
Hallelujah, Father, we give You praise
     E
For all You are.
          A              F♯m7                    D2
(And) Hallelujah, Jesus, we love Your name,
     E/G♯                [To Mid section,  Eadd4]
For all You've done.
```

Mid section:

```
     A/C♯  D2          F♯m7   Eadd4
And I will give You all my praise;
     A/C♯  D2       F♯m7         Eadd4
And I will sing of Your great name.  [Repeat x3]
```

Last chorus:

```
A              F♯m7                    D2
Hallelujah, Father, we give You praise
     E
For all You are.
          A              F♯m7                    D2
(And) Hallelujah, Jesus, we love Your name,
     Eadd4             A
For all You've done.
```

24. GIVE UNTO THE LORD
(Glorify the King)

Luke Finch

Verse:

G   C G/B Am G   C2   Am7
Give unto the Lord, O you mighty ones.
G   C   G/B Am G   C2
Give unto the Lord strength and glo - ry.
G   C   G/B Am G   C2   Am7
Give unto the Lord the glo - ry due his name.
G   C   G/B   Am G   C2
Worship the Lord in the beauty of his ho - liness.
           Am   G   D
For our God of glory thunders over many waters.
             Am   Em   D
Yes, our God of glory is powerful and full of majesty.

Chorus:

            G   D
So we glorify the King,
  Em   C
Glorify the King,
  G   D
Glorify the King,
  Em   C   [C2]
Glorify the King. [***Repeat***]

  G   D/F♯
Glory, glory, glory, glory,
  Em   C
Everyone in his temple cries out. [***Repeat***]

This song is recorded on the Spring Harvest 'Perfect Sacrifice - New Songs 2009' album

GOD WHOSE VOICE CALLED WORLDS 25.

(Through Jesus' eyes)

Graham Kendrick

Intro: D Bm G D

Verse 1:

```
D
God whose voice called worlds from nothing,
G                   Asus4   D
Lit the sun, made day and night;
                 Bm          A
Speak into this present darkness,
G       D       Asus4    D
Once again let there be light.
Bm     A/C# D    G      Bm       A
   Rise on us now       in this dark hour.
```

Chorus:

```
Bm7           A  G                 D  G        D       Em       A
God All–seeing, God All–knowing, heal our vision, make us wise;
Bm7                F# G      D       Bm  D                        A      [Bm]   [4. Chorus repeat  Bm7  G  A]
Cleanse, renew, revive, inspire us     to see the world through Jesus' eyes,
Bm7/A      G A    D   Bm   G   D
   Through Jesus's eyes.
```

Verse 2:

```
D
Show us in each face Your image
G                    Asus4   D
Stamped in sacred likeness there.
                  Bm          A
Scars of sin and death may ravage,
G          D        D/A    D
Faith has eyes for treasure rare.
Bm     A/C# D    G         Bm      A
   And all around       sees harvest now.
```

Verse 3:

```
D
Christ whose heart beat with compassion,
G                    Asus4 D
Yet with righteous anger burned,
              Bm          A
Walk in majesty among us,
G        D      Asus4 D
Let the fear of God return.
Bm     A/C#  D G        Bm            A
   And beautify      Your Church, Your Bride.
```

Verse 4:

```
 D
God whose Spirit searches all things,
G                  Asus4      D
Nothing hidden from Your gaze.
                    Bm           A
Grant that we may know the mind of
G           D         Asus4   D
Christ. For these momentous days
Bm A/C#    D    G     Bm       A
   Equip us now      to meet this hour.
```

26. GONNA DANCE, DANCE

(Dance)

Tim Hughes

Chorus 1:

```
        C/E    F       Am                G
Gonna dance, dance,  everybody dance.
        C/E    F       Am                G
Gonna dance, dance, everybody dance.
        C/E    F       Am                G
Gonna dance, dance, everybody dance.
        C/E    F       Am                G      C
Gonna dance, dance,  everybody dance now.
```

Chorus 2:

```
        C/E   F       Am                G
Gonna shout, shout,  everybody shout.
        C/E    F       Am                G
Gonna shout, shout,  everybody shout.
        C/E    F       Am                G
Gonna shout, shout,  everybody shout.
        C/E    F       Am               G      C
Gonna shout, shout,  everybody shout now.
```

Verse 1:

```
F                    G       C
   Your grace is overwhelming,
F                  G          C
   Your joy is in my heart,
F                        G       C           Dm7
   Your goodness lasts for evermore;
     F
And everybody sing:
```

Verse 2:

```
F                  G        C
   Your love is all consuming,
F                  G           C
   Your song is in my heart;
F                             G      C          Dm7
   You've changed this life for evermore;
     F
And everybody sing:
```

Chorus 3:

```
        C/E   F      Am                G
Gonna jump, jump, everybody dance.
        C/E   F      Am                G
Gonna jump, jump, everybody dance.
        C/E   F      Am                G
Gonna jump, jump, everybody dance.
        C/E    F        Am               G     C  F    Am   G   C
 Gonna jump, jump, everybody jump, now.
```

This song is recorded on the Spring Harvest 'Journey - Live Worship 2009' album

HALLELUJAH

27.

Ben Cantelon

Capo 2

```
      Em    C          G      D/F♯
Hallelujah,         hallelujah.
            Em       C             A        D/F♯
You are worthy         of our praise.
      Em    C          G      D/F♯
Hallelujah,         hallelujah.
            Em       C             A        D/F♯
You are worthy         of our praise.
```

```
Em
   Be high and lifted up,
C
   Be high and lifted up,
G                              D/F♯
   Be high and lifted up,       Jesus.
Em
   It's You we glorify,
C
   It's You we're lifting high.
G
   Your name be glorified.   [Repeat]
```

```
      Em    C          G      D/F♯
Hallelujah,         hallelujah.
            Em       C             A        D/F♯
You are worthy         of our praise.
      Em    C          G      D/F♯
Hallelujah,         hallelujah.
            Em       C             A
You are worthy         of our praise.
```

This song is recorded on the Spring Harvest 'Journey - Live Worship 2009' album

28. HAVE YOU HEARD

Capo 3

Simon Brading, Graham Kendrick
& Nathan Fellingham

Verse 1:

Em C D Em
Have you heard of a God of love,
C G D
Of a God who cares?
Em C D Em
Have you heard how he came among us,
C G D Em
Stepping down from the heights of heav'n,
C G D
Breathing air he made.

Verse 2:

Em C D Em
Have you heard he was one of us,
C G D
Shared our joy and tears?
Em C D G D/F♯
Did you know he restored the broken,
Em C D Em
Healed the lame, made the blind to see;
C G D
Brought his kingdom near.

Chorus:

Cmaj7 Dadd4 G Cmaj7
Oh, the love, the love that God has shown;
Em D/F♯ C/G G
Oh, the joy of forgiveness.
C/E D/F♯ G Cmaj7
Come, oh come, let us kneel before the cross;
D Cmaj7 [Em C D Em C G D **x2**]
[**1.**] This is love, this is love.
D Cmaj7
[**2.**] This is love, this is love,
D G G/F♯
This is love, this is love.

Verse 3:

Em C D Em
Have you heard he was crucified
C G D
On a Roman cross?
Em C D Em
Did you know that he chose to suffer,
C G D Em
To restore a creation lost;
C G D
Bearing all the cost.

Verse 4:

Em C D Em
Have you heard he was raised to life,
C G D
Bursting from the grave?
Em C D Em
Did you know that he saves forever
C G D Em
All who call on his mighty name,
C G D
On Jesus' name.

Last chorus:

Cmaj7 Dadd4 G Cmaj7
Oh, the love, the love that God has shown;
Em D/F♯ C/G G
Oh, the joy of forgiveness.
C/E D/F♯ G Cmaj7
Come, oh come, let us kneel before the cross;
D G
This is love, this is love,
Cmaj7 Dadd4 G Cmaj7
Oh, the love, the love that God has shown;
Em D/F♯ C/G G
Oh, the joy of forgiveness.
C B7 Em A/C♯ Am/C
Sing, oh sing, of the God who came to us:
D C
This is love, this is love. [***Repeat 4 times***]
G
This is love.

HE IS JEALOUS FOR ME

29.

(See His love)

Justin Byrne

Verse 1:

```
A
He is jealous for me;
F#m7
Love's like a hurricane, I am a tree,
E                                               D
Bending beneath the weight of His wind and mercy.
      A
When all of a sudden, I am unaware
            F#m7
Of these afflictions eclipsed by glory.
       E
And I realise just how beautiful You are,
          D
And how great Your affections are for me.
```

Bridge: (v.1 only)

```
     A                     F#m7
And oh, how he loves us so,
             E                        D      A   F#m7   E   D2
Oh, how he loves us, how he loves us so.
```

Verse 2:

```
A
We are his portion and he is our prize,
F#m7
Drawn to redemption by the grace in his eyes.
  E                           D
If grace is an ocean we're all sinking.
   A
So heaven meets earth like an unforseen kiss,
         F#m7
And my heart turns violently inside of my chest.
      E
And I don't have time to maintain these regrets
         D
When I think about the way.
```

Chorus:

```
            A                     F#m7
(Yeah,) he loves us, oh, how he loves us,
             E                    D                  [Last x A]
Oh, how he loves us, oh, how he loves.  [1. & 3. Repeat]
```

This song is recorded on the Spring Harvest 'Glory - New Songs 2010' album

30. HERE INSIDE YOUR PRESENCE
(Burning ones)

Chris Quilala
& Jeffrey Kunde

Verse 1:

```
G                                                                                   D
Here inside Your presence, I'm taken by the wonder of You.
G                                                                             D
Here, inside Your glory, we give our lives wholly to You. [Repeat]
```

Chorus:

```
              Bm      F#m7   G
And we cry holy, holy are You.
                      F#m7  Bm
And we cry holy, holy are You.
```

Verse 2:

```
G                                                                             D
Your love, it burns inside, our hearts are satisfied by You.
G                                                                                   D
Your love is our reward, that's why we ask for more of You.
```

Chorus:

```
              Bm      F#m7   G
And we cry holy, holy are You.
                              F#m7      Bm
Our hearts are burning, burning for You.
```

Mid section:

```
G                                         A
   We are Your burning ones,
Bm                                     E
   We are consumed by You,
G                                  A
   We set our lives apart,
Bm                                 A/C#
   We are consumed by You still. [Repeat]
G
   So let this love be like a fire,
A
   Let our lives be like a flame,
Bm
   Fill our souls with Your desire,
A/C#                                        [End Gmaj7]
   Let our passion bring You fame. [Repeat]
```

This song is recorded on the Spring Harvest 'Glory - New Songs 2010' album

HOPE IS HERE

(Jesus saves)

31.

<u>**Capo 4**</u>

Tim Hughes
& Nick Herbert

Verse 1:

            G   C   G
Hope is here, shout the news to everyone,
         C   Em   C/G   G
It's a new day, peace has come: Jesus saves.
          C   G
Mercy triumphs at the cross,
              C   Em   C/G   G
Love has come to rescue us: Jesus saves.

Chorus 1:

         C   D   C
Hope is here, what a joyful noise we'll make,
          Em   D/F♯   D
As we join in heaven's song
         Em   C   G
To let all the world know that Jesus saves.
             D   Em   C   G
Raise a shout to let all the world know that Jesus saves.

Coda:

G   D   Em   C   D   Em   Am7
   You save, oh.

Verse 2:

           G   C   G
Free at last every debt has been repaid,
         C   Em   C/G   G
Broken hearts can be remade: Jesus saves.
          C   G
Sing above the storms of life,
              C   Em   C/G   G
Sing it through the darkest night: Jesus saves.

Chorus 2:

        C   D   C
Free at last, what a joyful noise we'll make, . . .

Mid section:

         D   Em
You save, You heal, restore, reveal
         C
Your Father's heart to us.
        D   Em
You rose to raise us from the grave;
           C   Am7
Your Spirit lives in us.

Sing it out,
           Em   C   G
To let all the world know that Jesus saves. . . .

This song is recorded on the Spring Harvest 'Glory - New Songs 2010' album

32. HOLY, HOLY IS THE LORD GOD ALMIGHTY

Graham Kendrick

Capo 3

Verse :

```
Am7  G              Am7             G
Holy, holy is the Lord God Almighty;
     Am7              Em7                   A/C#     D
The whole earth is filled with Your glo    -  ry.
Am7  G              Am7             G
Holy, holy is the Lord God Almighty;
     Am7              Em7                   A/C#     Dsus4    D
The whole earth is filled with Your glo    -  ry.
```

Chorus:

```
      G           C               A   A/C# D
Your kingdom come, Your will  be  done
        G              C     A     A/C#    D
On the earth, as it is in hea      -       ven;
        G/B    G            C               D      Gsus4    G   [1. Am7    G    Am7    G]
Let the whole earth be filled with Your glory.
```

Chorus 2:

```
 G           C               A   A/C# D
Your kingdom come, Your will  be  done
        G              C     A     A/C#    D
On the earth, as it is in hea      -       ven;
        G/B    G            C               D      Gsus4    G
Let the whole earth be filled with Your glory.
         G                  C           A        A/C#      D
Let the whole earth be filled, the whole earth be filled
        G/B    G            C               D      Em7    D2    Cmaj7
Let the whole earth be filled with Your glory.
      D    Em7    F2    Am7
Your glo  -  ry,
     D    Gsus4    G
Your glo  -  ry.
```

HOW GREAT IS YOUR LOVE

(All glory)

33.

Nikki Fletcher

Capo 3

Verse 1:

Em   D/F♯   G   Cmaj7   Dsus4   D
   How great is Your love, covers my sin and shame.
Em   D/F♯   G   Cmaj7   Dsus4   D
   In You I'm free; I stand restored, complete.
Cmaj7   D   G   D/F♯   C2
Jesus, my redeemer, You have made a way.

Chorus:

D   G/B   C
   All glory to God who is able,
D   G/B   C2
   All power and praise;
D   G/B   C
   Forever the earth will proclaim:
                 Dsus4 G2/B   C69
[**1. 2.**] You are mighty,   You are mighty.
                 Dsus4 G2/B   C
[**3.**]   You are mighty,   You are mighty.
                 D   G/B   C
        He is mighty,   he is mighty.
                 Dsus4 G2/B   C
[**4.**]   You are mighty,   You are mighty.
                 D   G/B   Cmaj7
        He is mighty,   he is mighty.

Verse 2:

Em   D/F♯   G   Cmaj7   Dsus4   D
How great is Your love, covers my sin and shame.
Em   D/F♯   G   Cmaj7   Dsus4   D
In You I'm free; I stand restored, complete.
Cmaj7   D   G   D/F♯   C2
Jesus, I surrender, lead me in Your ways.

Mid section:

              D   G/B   C
Lift him higher, he is mighty;
              D   G/B   C2
Lift him higher, he is God.   [***Repeat***]

34. I AM AN INSTRUMENT OF THE LIVING GOD

(Sweet, sweet sound)

<u>**Capo 3**</u>

Ed Cash
& Sarah Reeves

Verse 1:

        G   A   Bm
I am an instrument of the living God,
          G   Asus4   A
My life a melody to his name.
              G   A   Bm
More than the songs I sing, worship is everything:
        G   A   D   Dsus4   D
I live to glorify my King.

Chorus:

D   A/C♯
Hear the song of my life;
            Bm
Let it be a sweet, sweet sound,
            G
Let it be a sweet, sweet sound.
  D   A/C♯
I raise this anthem high;
            Bm
Let it be a sweet, sweet sound,
            G2
Let it be a sweet, sweet sound. (***1° to v.1***)

Verse 2:

              G   A   Bm
Through all the mire and clay You're washing me with grace;
          G   Asus4   A
You carry me, O Lord, through it all.
        G   A   Bm
So I will testify, even in the fire:
        G   A   D   Dsus4   D
I live to praise my Saviour.

Mid section:

    Em   Em/D
Let everything that has breath
              A/C♯   A
Praise the Lord,   praise the Lord.
     Em   Em/D   C   A/C♯
And all creation will sing   hallelujah.

This song is recorded on the Spring Harvest 'Glory - New Songs 2010' album

I AM CHOSEN

(Holding nothing back)

35.

Capo 4

Tim Hughes
& Martin Smith

Verse 1:

```
G
   I am chosen, I am free,
                                      Em     C
I am living for eternity,    free now forever.
G
   You pick me up, turn me around,
                                              Em
You set my feet on solid ground;
       C                G
Yours now forever.
```

Bridge:

```
C        Em                              D
   And nothing's gonna hold me back,
                                      C
Nothing's gonna hold me back,
Em                                  D
Nothing's gonna hold me back.
```

Chorus:

```
G                                                  D
   My chains fell off, my heart was free,
            Em                                D
I'm alive to live for You, I'm alive to live for You.  [Last x to Coda:]
G                                    D
   Amazing love, how can it be?
                 Em
You gave everything for me,
                   D                            Cmaj7
You gave everything for me, everything.
```

```
                   C
[Coda:] I give everything for You,
                   Em                                   Am6
        I give everything for You, everything.
```

Verse 2:

```
G
   You've washed my sin and shame away,
                                           Em     C
The slate is clean, a brand new day,  free now forever.
G
   Now boldly I approach Your throne,
                                                        Em
To claim this crown through Christ my own,
       C                G
Yours now forever.
```

Mid section:

```
                  C              D
And I'm free to live, free to give,
     Em
Free to be, I'm free to love You.  [x3]
```

36. I SEE YOUR FACE

(You're beautiful)

Phil Wickham

Verse 1:

```
A                     D                  F♯m7                          Esus4     E
   I see Your face in every sun rise, the colours of the morning are inside Your eyes.
A                             D                 F♯m7                   Esus4         E
   The world awakens in the light of the day, I look up to the sky and say:  You're beautiful.
```

Chorus:

```
     A   D    F♯m7    Esus4          E
                             You're beautiful.
     A   D    F♯m7    Esus4          E
                             You're beautiful.
```

Verse 2:

```
A                          D                     F♯m7                           Esus4       E
   I see Your power in the moonlit night, where planets are in motion and galaxies are bright.
A                         D                    F♯m7                         Esus4          E
   We are amazed in the light of the stars;  it's all proclaiming who You are:   You're beautiful.
```

Verse 3:

```
A                           D              F♯m7                                        Esus4      E
   I see You there hanging on a tree, You bled and then You died and then You rose again for me.
A                     D                            F♯m7                         Esus4          E
   Now You are sitting on Your heavenly throne; soon we will be coming home:   You're beautiful.
```

Verse 4:

```
A                     D                       F♯m7                        Esus4       E
   When we arrive at eternity's shore, where death is just a memory and tears are no more,
A                       D                         F♯m7                                   Esus4          E
   We'll enter in as the wedding bells ring; Your bride will come together and we'll sing:   You're beautiful.
```

Tag:

```
A                          D                 F♯m7                Esus4     E
   I see Your face, You're beautiful, You're beautiful, You're beautiful.  [Repeat 3x]
A                          D                 F♯m7                Esus4     E    A
   I see Your face, You're beautiful, You're beautiful, You're beautiful.
```

I STAND AMAZED

37.

(Jesus died my soul to save)

Matt Bowell

Verse 1.

C G/B Am
I stand amazed at Your love for me;
F G C
That lonely night in Gethsemane.
G/B Am
This sinner's heart can't help but thrill
F G C
To hear You pray: "Father, not my will".

Chorus:

F C/E
What depth of love, what reach of grace;
Am G F
Oh, how my grateful heart now aches
C/E F C/E
To sing it louder, the refrain:
F Gsus4 G C
Jesus died my soul to save.

Verse 2:

F/G C G/B Am
Atonement full, applied to me,
F G C
The blood that spilled at Calvary
G/B Am
Has swallowed all my guilt and shame;
F G C
Now reconciled in Jesus' name.

Mid section:

G Am Fmaj7
Oh, such pleasure, oh, such pain;
G Am Fmaj7
The Father's wrath and fury laid,
G Am Fmaj7
On Christ whom saints and angels praise:
Dm7 C/E F2
Jesus died my soul to save.

Verse 3:

C G/B Am
Come ye broken, bound by sin,
F G C
Let your weary journey end.
G/B Am
Come and lay Your burden down
F G C
Where mercy rules and peace abounds.

38. I WILL EXALT YOU

Brooke Ligertwood

Verse 1:

  D   D/F♯ G2
I will ex - alt You,
  D   D/F♯ G2
I will ex - alt You,
  D   D/F♯ G2
I will ex - alt You,
       A   D
You are my God. [***Repeat***]

Chorus:

      A   Em7
My hiding place, my safe refuge,
      A/C♯   D
My treasure, Lord, You are.
      A
My Friend and King,
      Em7 D   G   Bm   A
Anointed   One, most holy. [***Repeat***]

Verse 2:

     D   D/F♯   G2
Because You're with me,
     D   D/F♯   G2
Because You're with me,
     D   D/F♯   G2
Because You're with me,
  A   D
I will not fear. [***Repeat***]

I WILL CAST MY CARES

39.

(Redeemer)

Cathy Burton

Verse 1:

                    C   D   G
I will cast my cares upon You, God,
                   C   D   G
Laying all my burdens at Your cross;
                 C   D
I will not be proud of all I've done
Em   D   C2   Cmaj7
    But I'll boast in You.

Verse 2:

                     C   D   G
I will place my heart into Your hands,
                      C   D   G
For You are the Author of my life,
                      C   D
And with every breath You give to me
Em   D   Cmaj7
    I will trust in You.

Chorus:

                       C2   D2   G
You are my redeemer, You are my healer,
                     C2   D2   G
You are my Saviour, You are my God.
                       C2   D2   Em   D/F♯
You are my Defender, the source of every hour.
                    C2   D2   [**1. 3.** Em   G   C   Em   G   Cmaj7]
You are my reason, You are my God. [**2.** Gsus4   G   Gsus4   G]

I will place my . . .

Mid section:

Am7   C2
Jesus, my Redeemer,
G   D   Dsus4   D
Ransomed now I stand.
Am7   C2
Jesus, my Redeemer,
G   D
You have won me back.
            Am7   C
My Redeemer, my Saviour,
          Em   D
My Comforter and Rescuer.

You are my . . .

40. I WILL NOT BOAST OF ANYTHING
(Jesus is alive today)

Stuart Barbour

Verse 1:
D
I will not boast of anything, but Jesus Christ my Lord and King.

So let his name be lifted high; the crucified, the one who died.

Verse 2:
D
I'll keep my eyes fixed on the One the Father sent to save the lost,

Who lived a blameless, holy life and freely made this sacrifice.

Bridge 1:
```
        G                     D
But the grave could not hold him,
         Bm                    A
And the earth began to shake;
        G               D
On the third day he arose,
    Bm                  A
The Saviour of the world.
```

Chorus:
```
D          G
Jesus is alive today;
    A                  G
The King of love, the risen Son.
D          G
Jesus is alive today,
A                G         [D]
Celebrate the holy One.
```

Verse 3:
D
Amazing love, how can it be, that Jesus Christ would die for me?

My chains fell off, my heart was free, I rose, went forth and followed Thee.

Bridge 2:
```
        G                     D
For the grave could not hold him,
         Bm                    A
And the earth began to shake;
        G               D
On the third day he arose,
    Bm                  A
The Saviour of the world.
```

Coda:
D
Celebrate. Celebrate.
Celebrate. Celebrate.

This song is recorded on the Spring Harvest 'Glory - New Songs 2010' album

I'LL REMEMBER YOU

41.

(Remember)

<u>**Capo 2**</u>

Tim Hughes
& Rachel Hughes

Verse 1:

D Gsus2/D A(no3rd)/D
I'll remember You,
D Gsus2/D A(no3rd)/D
I'll remember what You did.
D Gsus2/D
Remembering the cross,
Bm G2
Remembering the price You paid,
D Gsus2/D A(no3rd)/D
I'll remember You.

Chorus:

Gmaj7 Asus4 D/F♯
For no one's ever loved me quite like You do,
Gmaj7 Asus4 Bm
No one's ever loved me quite like You;
Gmaj7
Jesus, for Your glory,
Asus4 D/F♯ Gsus2
I will tell the story of the cross.

Coda:

Gsus2 [D Gsus2/D A/D ***x2***] D

Verse 2:

D Gsus2/D A(no3rd)/D
I will sing of You,
D Gsus2/D A(no3rd)/D
I will sing of what You did.
D Gsus2/D
The stone lies rolled away,
Bm G2
Nothing but an empty grave.
D Gsus2/D A(no3rd)/D
I will sing of You.

Mid section:

G A Bm A
Hallelujah, hallelujah, hallelujah for the cross.
G A Bm Asus4 A
Hallelujah, hallelujah, hallelujah for the cross.

42. I'M CASTING MY CARES ASIDE

(Today is the day)

Lincoln Brewster
& Paul Baloche

Verse 1:

                    D   Bm7   Asus4
I'm casting my cares aside,
   G2   D   Bm7   Asus4
I'm leaving the past behind,
   G2   D   Bm7   Asus4 G2   Em7   G2
I'm setting my heart and mind on You,   Jesus.

Bridge:

                     D   Bm9   Asus4
I'm reaching my hands to Yours,
  G2   D   Bm9   Asus4
Believing there's so much more,
G2   D   Bm9   Asus4   G2   Em7   G
Knowing that all You have in store for me is good,   it's good.

Chorus:

               D   A/C#   Bm7   G2
Today is the day You have made,   I will rejoice and be glad in it.
               D   A/C#   Bm7   G2
Today is the day You have made,   I will rejoice and be glad in it.
     Em7   D/F#   G   A
And I won't worry about tomorrow; I'm trusting in what You say.
                     D   Bm7   Asus4   G2   D   Bm7   Asus4
Today is the day,   today is the day.

Verse 2:

                    D   Bm7   Asus4
I'm putting my fears aside,
   G2   D   Bm7   Asus4
I'm leaving my doubts behind,
   G2   D   Bm7   Asus4 G2   Em7   G2
I'm giving my hopes and dreams to You,   Jesus.

Mid section:

D2
I will stand upon Your truth. (I will stand upon Your truth.)

And all my days I'll live for You. (All my days I'll live for You.)

I will stand upon Your truth. (I will stand upon Your truth.)
                                              Em   C   G
And all my days I'll live for You. (All my days I'll live.)

Coda:

      G   A
I'm giving You my fears and sorrows.
     Em   D/F#
Where You lead me, I will follow;
     G   A   D   Bm7   Asus4
I'm trusting in what You say: today is the day.
   G2   D   Bm7   Asus4   G2   D   Bm7   Asus4
Today is the day.   Today is the day.
   G2   D   Bm7   Asus4   G2   D2
Today is the day.   Today is the day!

This song is recorded on the Spring Harvest 'Glory - New Songs 2010' album

I'M NOT BACKING DOWN 43.

(Give us Your courage)

Tim Hughes

Verse 1:

```
Em
   I'm not backing down,
C
   I will stand my ground
G                  D
   lifting high the name of Jesus.
Em
   Holding out Your light
C
   To a world in need,
G                 D         Am7
   Living out the love of Jesus.
```

Bridge:

```
              G/B  C    Am7               G/B     C
Though the battles rage,    Your blessing still will come.
```

Chorus:

```
           G
To the ends of the earth we will go,
           D
To the ends of the earth we will go;
              Am                  C
Fill us with power, fill us with power.
            G
For the truth of Your word we will stand,
            D
For the truth of Your word we will stand;
                Am                    C
Give us Your courage, give us Your courage.
```

Coda:

```
Em    C    G   D    Em    C    G   D    Em
Whoah,     Whoah.   Whoah,     Whoah.
```

Verse 2:

```
Em
   Be our strength and song,
C
   Till the battle's won,
G                     D
   Cause Your face to shine upon us.
Em
   Stretch Your hand to save,
C
   Our God never fails
G                  D            Am7
   Nothing is impossible for Him
```

Mid section:

```
             D          C                G/B       Am
Would You breathe on us, would You breathe on us,
          D            C               G/B       Am7   G/B  C   D
Would You breathe on us, would You breathe on us.              To the ends . . .
```

This song is recorded on the Spring Harvest 'Journey - Live Worship 2009' album

44. IN THE BEGINNING
(Breath of God)

Vicky Beeching

Capo 3

***Verse 1*:**
Em   C   G   D/F♯
In the beginning was darkness and nothing,
        Em   C   D
Your Spirit was moving over the deep.
Em   C   G   D/F♯
You spoke a whisper and creation existed,
Em   C
Birthed by the mighty words that You speak.

Bridge:
                 Am7   G2/B   C   D/F♯
Just say the word and my weary soul will be renewed.

Chorus:
G   D/F♯
Breathe on me O breath of God
        Am7   G2/B Dsus4
And fill me with life anew.
G   D/F♯
Breathe on me O breath of God
      Am7 G2/B C   Dsus4   G
And set   this   heart on fire for You.

Verse 2:
Em   C   G   D/F♯
Bones in a valley were changed into an army,
Em   C   D
Raised by Your Spirit's powerful touch.
Em   C   G   D/F♯
Here in Your presence, I'm needing Your refreshing;
Em   C
Lord, please revive my heart with Your love.

Mid section:
   C   D   C   D
Revival fire, fall down like the rain.
   C   D   C   D
Revival fire, set my soul ablaze.
   C   D   C/E   D/F♯
Revival fire, fall down like the rain.
    C   D   C/E   D/F♯ C
Revival fire, set my soul ablaze.

This song is recorded on the Spring Harvest 'Journey - Live Worship 2009' and 'Perfect Sacrifice - New Songs 2009' album

IT'S FALLING FROM THE CLOUDS

(Cannons)

Phil Wickham

Verse 1:

```
    A                      E
It's falling from the clouds,
  Bm                       F#m
A strange and lovely sound,
 D              A           E
I hear it in the thunder and rain.
    A                E
It's ringing in the skies,
     Bm                  F#m
Like cannons in the night,
    D              A           E
The music of the universe plays.
```

Chorus:

```
     We're singing:
     A            D
     You are holy, great and mighty;
         F#m                    E
     The moon and the stars declare who You are.
         A                 D
     I'm so unworthy, but still You love me;
[1.]       F#m                E                          A    D    F#m   Bm
     Forever my heart will sing of how great You are.
[2.]       F#m                E
     Forever my heart will sing of You.
[3.]       F#m                E               A
     Forever my heart will sing of You. And You are . . .
[Coda:]    F#m                E                          A    D    F#m   Bm   A   D   F#m  E  D  A
     Forever my heart will sing of how great You are.
```

Verse 2:

```
 A                 E
Beautiful and free,
Bm              F#m
Song of galaxies,
    D            A               E
It's reaching far beyond the Milky Way.
     A                  E
Let's join in with the sound,
    Bm                F#m
C'mon, let's sing it out,
       D              A           E
As the music of the universe plays.
```

Mid section:

```
   D                              A      E
All glory, honour, power is Yours, amen.
   D                              A      E
All glory, honour, power is Yours, amen.
   D                            F#m      Esus4   E   Esus2   E   A
All glory, honour power is Yours forever, amen.                  You are . . .
```

This song is recorded on the Spring Harvest 'Glory - New Songs 2010' album

46. JESUS YOU ENDURED MY PAIN

(Because of Your love)

Capo 3

Phil Wickham

Verse 1:
D Dmaj7 D Dmaj7
Jesus, You endured my pain,
Bm Bm7 Bm
Saviour You bore all my shame,
Bm7 G Gmaj7 G Gmaj7
All because of Your love.
D Dmaj7 D Dmaj7
Maker of the universe,
Bm Bm7 Bm
Broken for the sins of the earth,
Bm7 G Gmaj7 G
All because of Your love,
Gmaj7 Bm Bm7 A
All because of Your love.

Chorus:
D A
Because of Your cross, my debt is paid;
Bm G
Because of Your blood, my sins are washed away.
D A
Now all of my life I freely give,
[1.] Bm G D A Bm G
Because of Your love, because of Your love, I live.
[2.] Bm G
Because of Your love, because of Your love. [***Repeat***]
[3.] Bm G Bm D A G Bm D A
Because of Your love, because of Your love, I live.
[4.] Bm G D
Because of Your love, because of Your love, I live.

Verse 2:
D Dmaj7 D Dmaj7
Innocent and holy King,
Bm Bm7 Bm
You died to set the captives free,
Bm7 G Gmaj7 G Gmaj7
All because of Your love.
D Dmaj7 D Dmaj7
Lord, You gave Your life for me,
Bm Bm7 Bm
So I will give my life for You,
Bm7 G Gmaj7 G
All because of Your love,
Gmaj7 Bm Bm7 A
All because of Your love.

Mid section:
A Em Bm
You did it for me, You did it for love;
D A
It's Your victory, Jesus, You are enough. [***Repeat***]

JESUS, BEAUTIFUL SAVIOUR

47.

(Beautiful Saviour)

Henry Seeley

Verse:

A   E/G♯   F♯m7
Jesus, beautiful Saviour,
A/E   D   A/C♯ Bm
God of all majesty, risen   King.
             A   E/G♯   F♯m7
Lamb of God, holy and righteous,
A/E   D   A/C♯   Bm
Blessed Redeemer, Bright Morning   Star.
          E   A/C♯   D
All the heavens shout Your   praise,
        E   A/C♯   D   D/F♯ E
All creation bows to worship You.

Chorus:

       A   E/G♯   F♯m7
How wonderful,   how beautiful,
A/E   D   A/C♯ Bm7 D/F♯   E/G♯
Name above every name, ex - alted high.
A   E/G♯   F♯m7
How wonderful,   how beautiful,
A/E   D   Bm7
Jesus, Your name,
                     D D/F♯ Esus4 E   Asus4   A   Asus4   A
Name above ev - ery name: Je   -   sus.

Mid section:

A   E/G♯ F♯m7
I will sing for - ever,
A/E   D   A/C♯   Bm   Esus4   E
Jesus I love You, Jesus I love You.

48. JESUS, MY PASSION IN LIFE

(Above all else)

Vicky Beeching

Verse:

```
D                                        Bm
Jesus, my passion in life is to know You.
                                   Em
May all other goals bow down to
       G              Asus4          D
This journey of loving You more.
D                                                  Bm
Jesus, You've showered Your goodness on me,
                            Em
Given Your gifts so freely.
      G                    Asus4           D
But there's one thing I'm longing for.
Em7                  D/F♯        G                      Asus4    A
Hear my heart's cry, and my prayer for this life.
```

Chorus:

```
D/G              D/F♯
   Above all else,
Em                  A
   Above all else,
G                D/F♯
   Above all else,
Em                      [D]
   Give me Yourself.
```

This song is recorded on the Spring Harvest 'Journey - Live Worship 2009' album

LET THE WORDS OF MY MOUTH 49.

(All for You)

Paul Baloche
& Graham Kendrick

Capo 4

```
          C
Let the words of my mouth
           Am
And the works of my hands
       F                 C
Be for You, Lord, all for You.
          Am
Let my hours and my days
        D/F♯
Be as worship and praise
     F                C   [Csus4   C]
For You, Lord, all for You. [Repeat]


                 E                  Am
Jesus, take my skill, my time,
                 F                  C
All of me, my strength, my mind.
                  Dm        Am
Lord, I want to work beside You
      F              Am G
And learn of You, Je - sus
     F         Am       F
Till all I do speaks of You.


          C
Let the words of my mouth
           Am
And the works of my hands
       F                 C
Be for You, Lord, all for You.
          Am
Let my hours and my days
        D/F♯
Be as worship and praise
     F                C
For You, Lord, all for You,
        F/C
Be for You, Lord,
          C           F/C   C
All for You, all for You.
```

This song is recorded on the Spring Harvest 'Glory - New Songs 2010' album

50. LIFE COULD TAKE
(Perfect sacrifice)

Lyrics: Nigel Briggs
Music: Trent

Chorus:

G   D/F♯
Life could take, take every dream away,
                          C
You'd still be my risen One,
                              G
The place where my hope comes from.
                                                D/F♯
Life could break, You'd still be my saving grace,
                      C
My promise of all to come,
                              G
The place where my hope comes from.

Verse 1:

            G   D/F♯
I've been chosen by Your hand,
                                              C
Through forgiveness called Your friend,
                                  G
Now You're here with me.
           G   D/F♯
Loosed my chains and took my shame,
                                    C
On the cross You bore my pain.
                    G
Jesus died for me.

Verse 2:

        G   D/F♯
It's a gift we don't deserve,
                                C
A treasure we cannot earn,
                        G
You paid the price.
          G   D/F♯
Now a life that offers more
                                   C
And a cross that's said it all,
                       G
A perfect sacrifice.

Coda:

G   D/F♯
All my hope is in You,
                        C
My treasure and my truth,
                       G
My hope is in You. [***Repeat***]

This song is recorded on the Spring Harvest 'Perfect Sacrifice - New Songs 2009' album

LOOK INSIDE THE MYSTERY

(Glorious)

Paul Baloche
& Brenton Brown

Verse 1:

```
C                            Em  Am
Look inside the mystery,        see the empty cross;
C/G                               F2
See the risen Saviour,       victorious and strong.
C                          Em   Am
No one else above him,        none as strong to save;
C/G                               F2
He alone has conquered        the power of the grave.
```

Chorus:

```
      F                                              C
Glorious,        my eyes have seen the glory of the Lord.
      F                                          C
Glorious,        he stands above the rulers of the earth.
```

Verse 2:

```
C                                 Em  Am
Look beyond the tombstone,        see the living God;
C/G                          F2
See the resurrected        ruler of my heart.
C                            Em  Am
No one else above him,         none to match his worth;
C/G                                 F2
The hope of his returning         fills the universe.
```

Mid section:

```
        G                  Am
Glorious,         glorious,
           F                 C   Cmaj7   Am   F   C   Cmaj7   Am   F
Lord, You are         glorious.
C   Cmaj7   Am                 F
Oh,                      You are glorious.
C   Cmaj7   Am                 F        [Last time:  C]
Oh,                      You are glorious.
```

52. LORD, MY LIFE IS AN EMPTY CUP

(Just to be with You)

Paul Baloche
& Jason Ingram

Verse 1:

```
          D          Bm7         Asus4
Lord, my life is an empty cup;
           D                     Bm7        Asus4
Here's my heart, would You fill me up.
                     G2                 Asus4
I'm face to the ground, forsaking my pride,
           G2                        Asus4    A
Leaving my will, my burdens behind.
```

Chorus:

```
A            D                 A/C♯
All I want,      all I need
             Bm7                    G2
Is just to be with You, just to be with You.
          D                  A/C♯
Here I am, at Your feet,
          Bm7                    G2
Just to be with You, just to be with You.
```

Coda:

Oh, all I want is just to be with You.

Verse 2:

```
       D               Bm7         Asus4
I have come to the end of me,
             D         Bm7            Asus4
And there's nothing I have to bring;
                   G2                    Asus4
But You say I belong, You say I am Yours;
             G2                         Asus4    A
Nothing compares to knowing You more
```

Mid section:

```
G                   D            Bm7   Asus4
You made a way for me,  O      Saviour,
G2           Bm7        Asus4
I'm Yours forever more.  [Repeat.]
G2           Bm7        Asus4    A
I'm Yours forever more.
```

LOVE THAT WILL NOT LET ME GO 53.

(All that I need)

Helen Gallagher

Verse 1:

```
D                     A/C#
Love that will not let me go,
 Bm                   A
I find my rest in You alone:
   G2          Asus4          G2         Asus4
I wait for You,         here I wait for You.
D                      A/C#
Love that fills my heart with peace,
        Bm                A
That calls the storm in me to cease:
    G2         Asus4          G2          A   Bm7   A/C#
I wait for You,          here I wait for You.
```

Chorus:

```
 D/F# G   D/F#    A/C#  Bm
In You I find all that I need.
     G     D/F#        Asus4   A
In You I am complete;
        G   D/F#   A/C#    Bm         G2
I am satisfied as long as You are near:
Em7            A        D   A/C#   Bm   A
You are my everything.
```

Verse 2:

```
D                      A/C#
Love that heals my brokenness,
  Bm                     A
Dries my tears and mends my heart:
    G2         Asus4           G2        Asus4
I wait for You,          here I wait for You.
D                     A/C#
Love that fills my heart with song,
    Bm               A
Held by You now I'll be strong:
   G2          Asus4          G2          A   Bm7   A/C#
I wait for You,         here I wait for You.
```

Chorus:

```
      D/F# G   D/F#    A/C#  Bm
      In You I find all that I need.
          G     D/F#        Asus4   A
      In You I am complete;
             G   D/F#   A/C#    Bm         G2
      I am satisfied as long as You are near:
      Em7            A        D   Em7   D/F#
[1.]  You are my everything.              [Repeat]
      Em7            A        D   A/C#   Bm   A   D
[2.]  You are my everything.
```

This song is recorded on the Spring Harvest 'Perfect Sacrifice - New Songs 2009' and 'Acoustic Worship' albums

54. MAY THE LORD BLESS YOU

Sam Hargreaves

```
               G2        Bm7  Asus4
May the Lord bless you,
D/F#           G2        Bm7  Asus4
May the Lord keep you,
D/F#             G2                  Bm7  Asus4
May the Lord's face shine down on you
        D/F#           D
And show you grace.
```

```
D/F#            G2        Bm7    Asus4
May the Lord  bless you,
D/F#           G2        Bm7  Asus4
May the Lord keep you,
D/F#          G2                   Bm7  Asus4
May the Lord turn his face to you
        D/F#          D
And give you peace.
```

```
                    G2    Bm7    Asus4
And give you peace,
         A          G2    Bm7    Asus4
And give you peace,
         A          G2    Bm7    Asus4
And show you grace,
         A          G2    Bm7    Asus4
And show you grace,
         A          G2    Bm7    Asus4
And give you hope,
         A          G2    Bm7    Asus4
And show you love,
         A          G2    Bm7    Asus4
And show you love,
         A          D
And give you peace,
```

.

MEEKNESS AND MAJESTY

(This is your God)

55.

Graham Kendrick

Verse 1:

```
C                 Am      Cmaj7           Am7
Meekness and majesty, manhood and deity,
C          Am            D7           G
In perfect harmony, the man who is God.
C         C/B♭  F                F♯dim7
Lord of eternity dwells in humanity,
Em               Am          F  C/G  G   C
Kneels in humility and washes our feet.
```

Chorus:

```
Dm         G
O what a mystery,
E7                Am       F
Meekness and majesty.
F♯dim7              C/G       Am    Dm
Bow down and worship
      G               B♭2     F
For this is your God,
[Last x        G               B♭2     F]
[Last x  For this is your God,]
G                  A♭   Gm7   C    G
This is your God.
```

Verse 2:

```
C                Am        Cmaj7     Am7
Father's pure radiance, perfect in innocence,
C          Am             D7          G
Yet learns obedience to death on a cross.
C               C/B♭          F                        F♯dim7
Suffering to give us life, conquering through sacrifice,
Em              Am                 F   C/G G  C
And as they crucify prays: 'Fa - ther forgive.'
```

Verse 3:

```
C             Am           Cmaj7      Am7
Wisdom unsearchable, God the invisible,
C           Am            D7       G
Love indestructible in frailty appears.
C          C/B♭   F                F♯dim7
Lord of infinity, stooping so tenderly,
Em              Am             F      C/G G  C
Lifts our humanity to the heights of His throne.
```

56. MORE THAN JUST ANOTHER SONG

(Listening)

Vicky Beeching

Verse 1:

                          D2   D/C♯
More than just another song,
                                 Bm9
More than one more melody,
                          G2
Maybe what we need is silence,
                                                     Aadd4
Maybe what we need is to be still.
                          D2
To listen for the still, small voice,
D/C♯   Bm9
   'Cause we don't want to miss a whisper,
                        G2   Em   Dmaj7/F♯   G2
Jesus, now we lean in closer, and we wait.

Chorus:

Aadd4 Bm7   G2   Aadd4
Speak,   Lord, Your servants are listening,
        Bm7   G2   Aadd4
Your servants are listening.
Aadd4 Bm7   G2   Aadd4
Speak,   Lord, Your servants are listening,
        Bm7   G2   [**1.** Bm9   G2   Aadd4   Bm7   G2]
Your servants are listening.

Verse 2:

                         D2   D/C♯
Lord, I want to know Your heart,
                        Bm9
Lord, I want to know what moves You,
                               G2
To understand what makes You weep,
                                                              Aadd4
To understand what makes You sing and smile.
                               D2
And this will be my life's one quest,
D/C♯   Bm9
   To seek the One whose love has sought me,
                          G2   Em   Dmaj7/F♯   G2
Gazing on Your shining beauty all my days.   So . . .

Mid section:

Aadd4   Bm9   G2
   What is   on Your   heart, O God, today?
Aadd9   Bm9   G2
    What is   on Your   mind, O God, today?
Aadd4   Bm9   G2
   What is   on Your   heart, O God, today?
Aadd9   Bm9   G2
    What is   on Your   mind, O God?

MY GOD IS GOOD 57.

Pete & Nicki Sims

Chorus:

```
D                  G   Bm7               Asus4   A
My God is good,      my God is good,
D                  G        Bm7            Asus
My God is good;    let my anthem ever be.
D                  G   Bm7              Asus4   A
My God is good,      my God is good,
D/F#                G        Bm7                  Asus4   A   [D   G   Bm7   Asus4   A]
My God is good;    how my God is good to me.
```

Verse 1:

```
      G             D/F#          G                       D
He is faithful to deliver on every promise he has made;
          G                       D/F#        Em7              Asus4   A
When I'm walking through the valley I don't have to be afraid.
```

Bridge:

```
    G                A
His love never fails,
        G/B              A/C#
Oh, His love never fails,
        G           Em7           A    Asus4   A
No, His love never fails, this I know.
```

Verse 2:

```
      G            D/F#          G                          D
He is mighty to deliver, he will keep You safe from harm,
       G                D/F#        Em7                  Asus4   A
By the power of the Spirit and the stretching of his arm.
```

Mid section:

```
D              G                    Asus4   A   D/F#             G
     Through joy and through pain,              he stays the same.
                      Asus4   A   D/F#            G
Seasons may change,               his love remains.
         Cmaj7                A/C#  D7            G
Through joy and through pain,         he stays the same.
Em7                   Asus4   A   D/F#            G
Seasons may change,               his love remains.
              Em     D      C     Asus4   A
For evermore         I will proclaim.
```

58. MY LORD, WHAT LOVE IS THIS

(Amazing love)

Graham Kendrick

Intro:

```
D    A/D    G/D    A/D   [Repeat]
```

Verse 1:

```
      D                    Em
My Lord, what love is this
        Asus4    A      Dsus4  D
That pays            so dear  -  ly,
A/D  D               Em
That  I, the guilty one,
G     A   D
May go free!
```

Chorus:

```
   Am7            Am/G   D
Amazing love, O what sacrifice,
      F                            A
The Son of God given for me.
      Am7              Am/G    D
My debt He pays, and my death He dies,
      Am7           D            Am7 G       D     G/D     D    [A/D]
That I       might live, that I       might live.
```

(***Last time only***)

```
       Am7  G       D
That I        might live!
```

Verse 2:

```
      D                          Em
And so they watched Him die,
     Asus4    A      Dsus4  D
Despised,          rejec  -  ted;
A/D D                    Em
But  oh, the blood He shed
G       A   D
Flowed for me!
```

Verse 3:

```
      D                    Em
And now, this love of Christ
       Asus4    A      Dsus4  D
Shall flow          like ri   -   vers;
A/D    D                   Em
Come wash your guilt away,
G     A D
Live again!
```

MY TIMES ARE IN YOUR HANDS
(I will hold on)

Nigel Briggs

Verse :

```
D2
   My times are in Your hands,
                                        D2/G
I know I'll never understand,
                        D2
But I'll trust in You.

Sometimes my heart grows cold,
                                        D2/G
I'm sorry when I take control,
                            D2
How I'm needing You.
```

Bridge:

```
                    Asus4
Even when I fall,
                    D2/G
You help me stand.
                    Asus4
Even when I'm lost,
                     D2/G
You take my hand.
```

Chorus:

```
           D
I will hold      on,
           D/G
I will hold      on,
           Bm7      A
I will hold      on,
     D/G                [Last x D/G   D]
Yes, I will trust in You.
```

Chorus: 3rd time

```
           D
I will hold      on,
           D/G
I will hold      on,
           Bm7      A   D/G   D   D/G   D   D/G
I will hold      on.
```

60. NOTHING CAN SEPARATE

(Your love never fails)

Chris McClarney
& Anthony Skinner

Verse 1:

```
Em                C
   Nothing can separate,
G              D/F#
   Even if  I ran away.
      Em               C    G    D
Your love never fails.
Em                C
   I know I still make mistakes, but
G                                  D/F#
   You have new mercy for me every day.
      Em              C    G    D    C
Your love never fails.
```

Chorus:

```
                     G                        D/F#
You stay the same through the ages;
   Am             G/B   C
Your love never changes.
                  G
There may be pain in the night,
     D/F#                       Am      C
But joy comes with the morning.
          G                  D/F#
And when the oceans rage
          Am              G/B    C
I don't have to be afraid
            G                          D/F#
Because I know that You love me
                                C    Em    D
And Your love never fails.
```

Verse 2:

```
Em                               C
   The wind is strong and the water's deep, but
G                                D/F#
   I'm not alone here in these open seas,
            Em                  C    G    D
'Cause Your love never fails.
Em                  C
    The chasm was far too wide,
G                                     D/F#
    I never thought I'd reach the other side;
         Em               C    G    D    C
 But Your love never fails.
```

Tag:

```
C                Em                          D
   All things    work together for my good.
          C          Em                          D
You make all things     work together for my good.
```

NOW UNTO THE KING WHO REIGNS OVER ALL 61.
(How great is Your faithfulness)

Jonas Myrin
& Matt Redman

Capo 2

Verse 1:

```
      C              G       D                  Em
Now unto the King     who reigns over all,
     C          G             D
And never changes or turns.
C             G     D               Em
Unfailing justice, unfading grace,
       C                   D
Whose promises remain,
           C           D
Yes, Your promises remain.  [Repeat.]
```

Chorus:

```
            G       D/F♯      Em         C
(Yes,) The heavens ring, the saints all sing,
G               D              Em   C
'Great is Your faithfulness.'
     G     D/F♯        Em       C
From age to age we will proclaim,
G                D            Em  C
'Great is Your faithfulness,   [2° & 4° Repeat. Last° to Coda]
     G               D                G    [D/F♯   Em   G   D/F♯   Em]
How great is Your faithfulness.'
```

Verse 2:

```
C              G           D                  Em
Everything changes, but You stay the same;
     C            G            D
Your Word and kingdom endure.
   C                G        D                  Em
We lean on the promise of all that You are,
     C           D
And trust forevermore;
          C           D
We will trust forevermore.
```

Mid section:

```
G     C     G         D    Em
From generation to generation,
C           G      D
You never fail us, O God.
C        G          D            Em
Yesterday and today and tomorrow,
   F                     Dsus4   D
Until the day You return.
```

Coda:

```
     G                  D               Em  C
'How great is Your faithfulness,
     G                  D            G   G2
How great is Your faithfulness.'
```

This song is recorded on the Spring Harvest 'Glory - New Songs 2010' album

62. OH, HOW COULD IT BE
(Remembrance)

Matt Redman & Matt Maher
Mid section words: taken from the English translation of the Memorial Acclamation from The Roman Missal

Verse 1:

```
   D
Oh, how could it be
         Asus4                  A     Em7
That my God would welcome me into this mystery?
                 D
Say, 'take this bread, take this wine,'
          Asus4          A        Em7
Now the simple made divine for any to receive.
```

Bridge:

```
          D/F♯            G            A
By Your mercy, we come to Your table;
          Em7               D/F♯         G
By Your grace, You are making us faithful.
```

Chorus:

```
              D    Bm7    A
Lord, we remember You,
         G               D           A
And remembrance leads us to worship.
              G   D        A
And as we worship You,
    G        D          A
Our worship leads to communion.
          Em7      D/F♯    G         [1.2. Bm7  A  D   [1. Dmaj7   Em7]
We respond to Your invitation; [we remember You.]
```

Coda:

```
 G         Em7     D/F♯    G              Bm7 A   D
We respond to Your invitation; we remember You.
```

Verse 2:

```
        D
See His body, his blood–
            Asus4      A             Em7
Know that he has overcome every trial we will face.
                 D
And none too lost to be saved,
           Asus4         A              Em7
None too broken or ashamed; all are welcome in this place.
```

Mid section:

```
D             G       A  D                        G     A   Bm
Dying, You destroyed our death. Rising,You restored our life.
                        A                               G      [D]
Lord Jesus, come in glory, Lord Jesus, come in glory.  [Repeat]
                        G   Dmaj7   Em7
Lord Jesus, come in glory.               By Your . . .
```

This song is recorded on the Spring Harvest 'Glory - New Songs 2010' album

O PRECIOUS SIGHT

(The wonder of the cross)

63.

Vicky Beeching

Capo 1

Verse 1:

              G   D/F♯   G   G/B
O precious sight, my Saviour stands, dying for me with outstretched hands.
              C2   D/F♯   Em7   Am   D/F♯   Em7
O precious sight; I love to gaze, remembering salvation's day,
            Am   D/F♯   G
Remembering salvation's day.

Verse 2:

                     G   D/F♯   G   G/B
Though my eyes linger on this scene, may passing time and years not steal
                    C2   D/F♯   Em7   Am   D/F♯ Em7
The power with which it impacts me, the freshness of its mystery,
              Am   D/F♯ G
The freshness of its mystery.

Chorus:

G   D/F♯
May I never lose the wonder,
      Am7   G
The wonder of the cross.
        Em7   D/F♯
May I see it like the first time,
           Am7   Em7
Standing as a sinner lost.
                C   G/B
Undone by mercy and left speechless,
             Am7   Em7
Watching wide-eyed at the cost.
        C   D/F♯   Em7
May I never lose the wonder,
      Am   D/F♯   G
The wonder of the cross.

Verse 3:

             G   D/F♯ G   G/B
Behold, the God - man crucified, the perfect sinless sacrifice.
              C2   D/F♯   Em7   Am   D/F♯ Em7
As blood ran down those nails and wood, history was split in   two,
              Am D/F♯ G
History was split   in   two.

Verse 4:

             G   D/F♯   G   G/B
Behold, the empty wooden tree, his body gone, alive and free.
               C2 D/F♯   Em7   Am   D/F♯   Em7
We sing with everlasting joy for sin and death have been destroyed,
         Am   D/F♯   G
Sin and death have been destroyed.

This song is recorded on the Spring Harvest 'Journey - Live Worship 2009', 'Acoustic Worship', 'He is risen indeed' and Wonderful Saviour - New Songs 2008' albums

64. ONCE I WAS DEAD TO YOU

(Promised land)

Lou and Nathan Fellingham
& busbee

Verse 1:

```
             D
Once I was dead to You and I could not hear.
      G                          C       D
I was blind to the truth and was nowhere near.

But then You gave me life and You gripped my soul
        G                     C        D
With a love so pure and You won't let go.
```

Chorus:

```
         D
What a Saviour, my Redeemer,
           G                   C     D
You have freed me, helped me understand.

Through Your suff'ring I'm forgiven,
          G              C        D
Pressing onward to the promised land.
```

Verse 2:

```
               D
Sent from his Father above,  Jesus walked this earth;
          G            C       D
Knew his destiny as he read the Word.

Not shrinking back from the task,  he pursued his goal;
         G                  C           D
Came to ransom lives and to make them whole.
```

Mid sectiom:

```
C                            G      D               A      C                  G
   You've bought me with a price,    a perfect sacrifice.    Now all I have I give to You.
C                 G          D             A        C                     G
   My life no longer mine,    to live or die is Christ.     Bound now for heaven.
```

Verse 3:

```
               D
Now with the Spirit's help I can journey on,
          G                        C      D
Knowing peace with God,  my convictions strong.

Because of Jesus' blood,  I am now secure
        G                 C       D
And because he lives, my hope is sure.
```

Last chorus:

```
D
Jesus, risen Saviour,
         G                C       D
He's our healer, death could not withstand.

His name is Jesus, sent from heaven
           G              C        D
To take us homeward to the promised land.
```

OPEN MY EYES 65.

(My soul sings)

Stuart Garrard, Martin Smith
& Jonathan Thatcher

Verse 1:

```
C                   G
Open my eyes and see
     Am                  F       C   Dm7   C/E   F
The wonderful mystery of love.
C               G
Falling into You,
    Am                   F        C   Dm7   C/E   F
I'm drawn to the gravity of love.
```

Bridge:

```
Dm                      G
   We're standing still
     Am           F
In a moment of eternity,
Dm                       G
   Where worlds collide,
       Am                          G/B     C
And I feel the breath of heaven over me.
```

Chorus:

```
              G                 Am
My soul sings, my soul sings,
              F                  C
My soul sings how I love You.
             G/D         C/E
My soul sings my soul sings,
             F                   C   [Dm7   C/E   F]
My soul sings how I love You.
```

Verse 2:

```
C                    G
Turn the page and see
     Am              F       C   Dm7   C/E   F
The wonderful history of love.
  C                   G
I start and end with You,
     Am                  F       C   Dm7   C/E   F
I'm pulled to the gravity of love.
```

66. ON THE DARK NIGHT

(Emmanuel God with us)

Vicky Beeching

Capo 3

Verse 1:

```
Em9                  Cmaj9
On the dark night that You were betrayed,
G/B                        D
You broke the bread in pieces;
Em9                 Cmaj9
You poured the wine, knowing Your life
      G2                    D/F♯
Would soon be poured out to heal us:
     Am7  G/B  Csus2
What love   is   this?
```

Chorus:

```
          D/F♯                C/E
    Emmanuel, You're God with us,
                       C2            G2/B           D/F♯
    And we remember You through Your body and Your blood.
                                C/E
    Emmanuel, You gave Your life,
                    Csus2              Em9   Cmaj9   G2   D/F♯
[1.] Our hearts cry thankYou for Your sacrifice.
                    Csus2              Am   Em7    Csus2  G   Dsus4   D
[2.] Our hearts cry thankYou for Your sacrifice.          Ooo.
                    C             D      C2
[3.] Our hearts cry thankYou for Your sacrifice.
```

Verse 2:

```
Em9                  Cmaj9
Why would You die for someone like me,
G/B                        D
someone so undeserving?
Em9                  Cmaj9
Why would You leave heaven's glory
      G2                    D/F♯
To step down and carry my burdens:
     Am7  G/B  Csus2
What love   is   this?
```

Mid section:

```
Am                        Em
Let Your blood cover me, wash me white and set me free;
C2                              G         D/F♯
Let Your blood make me clean today, today.
Am                        Em
Let Your blood cover me, wash me white and set me free;
C2                              G         D/F♯   Am7    G/B    C
Let Your blood make me clean today, today.                Emmanuel . . .
```

SEARCH MY HEART 67.

Stuart Barbour

Verse:

A   Asus4   A
Search my heart and know my thoughts,
F♯m   F♯sus4   F♯m
Shine Your light on my intentions,
                  D   Dsus4 D   A   Asus4   A
See if there be any wicked way in me that I must confess.
               Asus4   A
Holy Spirit fill me right up,
F♯m   F♯sus4   F♯m
Fill me with the Father's love
                  D   Dsus4 D   A   Asus4   A
So that I may walk into the light of God, always to serve him.

A
Precious are Your thoughts to me, O God,
         E(no3rd)
Your holy, Your righteous ways;
                    D
Lead me in Your everlasting love,
Bm7   A   E
Father above, I will serve You all my days.

      A
And if I climb up to the mountain tops,
        E
I know I will find You there;
                 D   Bm7
If ever to the valley I go, when my heart is low,
         A   E
You lift me from despair.
              D   Bm7 E
And Your banner over me is love,
               D   Bm7 E
Yeah,Your banner over me is love,
       D   Bm7   E   A   Asus4   A   Asus4   A
Your banner over me is love, is love.

68. SEE MARTHA WEEPING AT A TOMB
(God of compassion)

Simon Brading
& Graham Kendrick

Verse 1:
Em   D   Em   D
   See Martha weeping at a tomb;
C   G/B   C   G/B
   How deep the anguish of her grieving.
Em   D   Em   D
   Her brother, Lazarus, is gone,
C   G/B   C
   And hope lies cold and buried with him.
G/B   Am   Am7
And then Jesus comes.

Verse 2:
Em   D   Em   D
   See Mary stumbling through her tears,
C   G/B   C   G/B
   To meet the one who could have saved him.
Em   D   Em   D
   Why did it have to end this way?
C   G/B   C
   Did he not care her heart was breaking?
G/B   Am   C
And she falls facedown, in her deep despair;
         Em   D
Pours out her pain and His heart breaks.
            Am   C
Then His anger burns in the face of death:
       G/D   D
Jesus weeps, Jesus weeps.

Verse 3:
Em   D   Em   D
   There is no pain He does not know,
C   G/B   C   G/B
   No road of bitterness or sadness.
Em   D   Em   D
   No depths of sorrow we can go,
C   G/B C
   He walks the valley there beside us.
G/B   Am   C
Let us lift our eyes, look into the face
      Em   D
Of a God who knows, of God who weeps.
            Am   C
And His voice cries out, in the darkest place:
                  G/D   D
I am the Life,   I am the Life. [*to Chorus.*]

Chorus:
                   Am7   C/G   G
God of compassion,
            G   D
God of compassion is here.
                 Am7   C/G   G   G   D
God of all comfort   is here with us, has come to us;
                   Em [**1.** D   Em   D   C   G/B   C   G/B ***to Verse 3.***]
God of compassion.

Mid section:
G/B C   G/B C   G/D   Bm
And now He   lives, He is the life,   He is the life.
  C   G/B C   G/D   Bm
Alive in   Him, we'll never die,   never die. [***Repeat***]

Coda:
                   Em D   Em   C   G/B   C [**x2**]
God of compassion.

This song is recorded on the Spring Harvest 'Glory - New Songs 2010' album

THE GOD WHO SET THE STARS IN SPACE 69.

Words: Timothy DudleySmith
Tune: from Wurttemberg Gesangbuch,1784
arr. David Peacock

Verse 1:

```
     G                                  C        D       G
The God who set the stars in space and gave the planets birth
                                  C         D      G
Created for our dwelling place a green and fruitful earth;
C/G   G                     D                   G                D
A    world with wealth and beauty crowned of sky and seas and land,
        G                                  C       D7       G     C/G   G
Where life should flourish and abound beneath its Maker's hand.
```

Verse 2:

```
   G                               C        D   G
A world of order and delight God gave for us to tend,
                                    C       D      G
To hold as precious in his sight, to nurture and defend;
C/G   G             D                G                D
But  yet on ocean, earth and air the marks of sin are seen,
      G                           C    D7     G     C/G  G
With all that God created fair polluted and unclean.
```

Verse 3:

```
   G                                   C         D    G
O God by whose redeeming grace the lost may be restored,
                                        C         D      G
Who stooped to save our fallen race in Christ, creation's Lord,
C/G       G                  D                 G                D
Through him whose cross is life and peace to cleanse a heart defiled
      G                                    C     D7   G     C/G  G
May human greed and conflict cease and all be reconciled.
```

Verse 4:

```
    G                               C        D       G
Renew the wastes of earth again, redeem, restore, repair;
                                            C    D       G
With us, Your children, still maintain Your covenant of care.
C/G   G                    D               G                 D
May we, who move from dust to dust and on Your grace depend,
    G                                  C         D7     G       C/G  G
No longer, Lord, betray your trust but prove creation's friend.
```

Verse 5:

```
      G                                  C         D      G
Our God, who set the stars in space and gave the planets birth,
                                                   C         D      G
Look down from heav'n, Your dwelling place and heal the wounds of earth;
C/G   G               D                     G              D
'Til  pain, decay and bondage done, when death itself has died,
    G                                  C        D7  G
Creation's songs shall rise as one and God be glorified.
```

70. THERE IS AN EVERLASTING KINDNESS

(The compassion hymn)

Keith and Kristyn Getty
& Stuart Townend

Verse 1:

```
              G               D/F♯              Em7  G/A  D
There is an everlasting kindness You lavished on us,
            G               D/F♯                Em7  D/F♯ G  A7sus4
When the radiance of heaven came to res  -  cue  the lost.
                  G                     D/F♯           Em7      G/A     D
You called the sheep without a shepherd to leave their distress,
           G                D/F♯                 Em7       G/A   G    D/F♯    A    Bm7    A/C♯    D
For Your streams of forgiveness and the shade of Your rest.
```

Verse 2:

```
                  G                   D/F♯            Em7      G/A      D
And with compassion for the hurting You reached out Your hand,
          G              D/F♯                  Em7  D/F♯     G   A7sus4
As the lame ran to meet You and the dead breathed a - gain.
              G                    D/F♯          Em7   G/A   D
You saw behind the eyes of sorrow and shared in our tears;
            G              D/F♯              Em7       G/A  D
Heard the sigh of the weary, let the children draw near.
```

Chorus:

```
         A            A/G          D/F♯           G
What boundless love, what fathomless grace
              Em7            D/F♯     G    A  Bm7  A/C♯  D
You have shown us, O God of compas         -         sion.
         A        A/G    D/F♯          G
Each day we live an offering of praise
          Em7           D/F♯                    A7sus4  [G    D/F♯    A  Bm7  A/C♯  D x2]
As we show to the world Your compas   -   sion.
```

Verse 3:

```
                G                       D/F♯            Em7    G/A      D
We stood beneath the cross of Calvery and gazed on Your face,
          G              D/F♯              Em7    D/F♯ G  A7sus4
At the thorns of oppression and wounds of   disgrace;
              G                        D/F♯           Em7 G/A   D
For surely You have borne our suffering and carried our grief,
           G              D/F♯                      Em7      G/A  D
As You pardoned the scoffer and showed grace to the thief.
```

Verse 4:

```
               G                     D/F♯        Em7  G/A  D
How beautiful the feet that carry this gospel of    peace
           G            D/F♯                 Em7  D/F♯ G  A7sus4
To the fields of injustice and the val  -  leys of need;
             G                  D/F♯         Em7     G/A D
To be a voice of hope and healing, to answer the cries
          G              D/F♯                 Em7    G/A  D
Of the hungry and helpless with the mercy of   Christ.
```

THERE IS LOVE

(Stronger)

71.

Reuben Morgan
& Ben Fielding

Verse 1:

```
C         F            G        C/E
There is Love that came for us,
C           F    G     C/E
Humbled to a sinner's cross.
      C             F              G    Am
You broke my shame and sinfulness.
      G       F          G  Fmaj7   G   C/E   Cmaj7   Fmaj7   G   C/E
You rose again, victorious.
```

Verse 2:

```
C        F               G      C/E
Faithfulness, none can de  -  ny,
 C             F             G           C/E
Through the storm and through the fire.
C          F             G      Am
There is truth that sets me free:
G       F              G        C
Jesus Christ, who lives in me.
```

Chorus:

```
               C                      G
      You are stronger, You are stronger,
             Am                    F
      Sin is broken, You have saved me.
           C                   G
      It is written: 'Christ is risen'.
              F         G        Fmaj7   G   C/E   Cmaj7   Fmaj7   G   C/E
[1.] Jesus, You are Lord of all.
              F         G         F   Am   C/E   G/B   F   Am   C/E   G/B
[2.] Jesus, You are Lord of all.
              F         G         F
[3.] Jesus, You are Lord of all.
```

Verse 3:

```
C      F          G     C/E
No beginning and no end.
 C             F           G    C/E
You're my hope and my defence.
      C       F           G       Am
You came to seek and save the lost.
      G       F     G        C
You paid it all upon the cross.
```

Mid section:

```
    G              F
So let Your name be lifted higher,
Am7          G     C                  G
   Be lifted higher, be lifted higher. [Repeat]
```

72. THERE'S A NEW DAY DAWNING

(Jubilee)

Nigel Briggs
& Trent

Verse 1:

```
         G
There's a new day dawning now,
   C/G
A new song singing out;
   G
A river deep and wide,
                         C/G
His love is all around,
                        Em
His love is all around,
                   C
God is all around.
```

Verse 2:

```
      G
It's a time of jubilee.
     C/G
Young and old set free;
     G
And blind eyes now can see
                      C/G
God is on the move,
                      Em
God is on the move,
                         C
His love is on the move.
```

Chorus:

```
            G               C
      It's time to live the life,
                 Em            Bm             C
      For God's church to shine for Christ;

      Oh, tell the world of love
              G         D/F♯            Em
      Oh, beyond this flesh and blood,
[1. 2.]          C       Am7    G    C/G
      Oh, it's time to live the life.
[Coda:]          C          Am7                      G    C
      Oh, it's time yes, it's time to        live the life.
```

Mid section 1°:

```
G                C
Oh,       oh, oh, oh. [Repeat x8]
```

Mid section 2°:

```
   G                                                 C
So open the win dows of heaven, let Your love shine through, till the world knows You. [Repeat]
   Oh,                            oh,     oh,         oh.
```

THIS IS OUR SONG 73.

(Now and ever)

Nigel Briggs
& Trent

Verse:

```
             A                          F♯m9
This is our song, that Jesus is alive,
                                   Esus2
In a world that's losing ground,
             Dsus2
He is the lifeline.
            A                       F♯m9
He is our hope, for now and ever,
                            Esus2
The Son who never dies,
                             Dsus2    A    F♯m7    E    D2
No greater love in life.
```

Chorus:

```
A                      E
Jesus is alive today,
                   D                      A
See his saving grace, now and ever.
                           E
Jesus opened up the way
                          D
With truth that never fades:
                        [Last x A]
He'll reign forever.
```

Mid section:

```
F♯m
   Came to earth to be with us,
E
   Conquered death upon a cross,
D
   Son of God, the risen One;
         A
You're now and ever.
F♯m
   Opened eyes and hearts set free,
E
   Showed the world its destiny,
D
   Jesus Christ, the living King,
         Bm              D
You're now and ever.
```

74. THROUGH IT ALL

Capo 4

Matt Redman
& Jonas Myrin

Chorus:

```
               Am   Em       D
Through it all, You are faithful.
               Am    Em        D
Through it all, You are strong.
            Am       Em          D
As we walk through the shadows,
                      C2   Em     D
[1. 3.] Still You shine on,          oh.
                      C2   Em     D
[2.]     Still You shine on,         oh.
                      C2   Em     D
         Still You shine on.
```

Verse 1:

```
G                    Bm/F♯ Em   C
So many broken promises,
G                       Bm/F♯
So many empty words.
G                   Bm/F♯ Em   C
God of love and faithfulness,
      G                    Bm/F♯
Have mercy on this world.
```

Bridge:

```
            Dm              C
You never turn or change,
              Cm7        G/B
You never break the faith,
Dm                          C2
Yesterday, today and always.
```

Verse 2:

```
G                    Bm/F♯ Em   C
God of unbroken promises,
G                              Bm/F♯
Always You keep Your word.
G                 Bm/F♯ Em   C
Glory, grace and holiness
G                Bm/F♯
Forever to endure.
```

Through it all   Still You shine on.

Mid section:

```
         C  F  D
You are faithful, Jesus,
         Am     Em       D
You are faithful to the end.  [Repeat]
```

[***Last time***]

```
              Dm           C
You never turn or change,
              Cm7        G
You never break the faith.
```

TO GIVE AS YOU GAVE

(Here on the earth)

75.

Eoghan Heaslip
& David Ruis

Capo 4

***Verse*:**

```
G
  To give as You gave,
Am7
  To love as You loved,
C                         G      D/F#
  We will follow where You lead.
G
  To walk as You walked,
Am7
  To serve as You served,
C                         G      D/F#
  We will follow where You lead.
```

Bridge

```
C                D
  We pour out our lives in worship,
C              Em        D/F#
  Pour out our lives for You.
```

Chorus:

```
G
  Let Your kingdom come,
D/F#                   C
  Let Your will be done here on the earth,
                D
Here on the earth.
G
  Give us eyes to see,
D/F#                      C
  The courage to believe here on the earth,
             D/F#  [1. C2] [2. Gsus4   G]
Here on the earth.
```

Mid section:

```
C
  Bringing justice,
D
  Loving mercy,
Em                           [1. Bm]  [2. Bm  C2   G   Bm/F#   Cmaj7   Csus2]
  Walking humbly with our God.
```

76. TO SEE THE KING OF HEAVEN FALL

(Gethsemane)

Keith Getty
& Stuart Townend

Verse 1:

Bm F♯m/A Em/G Bm/F♯ Em7 F♯m7 B(no3rd)
To see the King of heaven fall in anguish to His knees,
Bm F♯m/A Em/G Bm/F♯ Em7 F♯m7 B(no3rd)
The Light and Hope of all the world now overwhelmed with grief.
D A/C♯ Bm Em/G F♯m/A D A/C♯ Bm Em/G F♯m/A
What nameless horrors must He see, to cry out in the gar - den:
Bm F♯m/A Gmaj7 Bm/F♯ Em7 F♯m7 Gsus2 G
'Oh, take this cup a - way from me!
Em7 F♯m7 Gsus2 G
Yet not my will but Yours,
Em7 F♯m7 B(no3rd)
Yet not my will but Yours.

Verse 2:

Bm F♯m/A Em/G Bm/F♯ Em7 F♯m7 B(no3rd)
To know each friend will fall away, and heaven's voice be still,
Bm F♯m/A Em/G Bm/F♯ Em7 F♯m7 B(no3rd)
For hell to have its vengeful day up - on Golgotha's hill.
D A/C♯ Bm Em/G F♯m/A D A/C♯ Bm Em/G F♯m/A
No words de - scribe the Saviour's plight, to be by God forsa - ken
Bm F♯m/A Gmaj7 Bm/F♯ Em7 F♯m7 Gsus2 G
Till wrath and love are sa - tis - fied,
Em7 F♯m7 Gsus2 G
And every sin is paid,
Em7 F♯m7 B(no3rd)
And every sin is paid.

Bm Bm/A Gmaj7 D/F♯ Em7 Dmaj7 C♯m7(♭5) F♯/E
Bm/D F♯m/A Gmaj7 D/F♯ Em7 Dmaj7 F♯7sus4 F♯7

Verse 3:

Bm F♯m/A Em/G Bm/F♯ Em7 F♯m7 B(no3rd)
What took Him to this wretched place, what kept Him on this road?
Bm F♯m/A Em/G Bm/F♯ Em7 F♯m7 B(no3rd)
His love for Adam's curséd race,for every broken soul.
D A/C♯ Bm Em/G F♯m/A D A/C♯ Bm Em/G F♯m/A
No sin too slight to overlook, no crime too great to car - ry,
Bm F♯m/A Gmaj7 Bm/F♯ Em7 F♯m7 Gsus2 G
All min - gled in this poi - soned cup,
Em7 F♯m7 Gsus2 G
And yet he drank it all,
Em7 F♯m7 Gsus2 G
The Saviour drank it all,
Em7 F♯m7 B(no3rd)
The Saviour drank it all.

TO YOU, O LORD

77.

Graham Kendrick

Verse 1:
E   B/E   A/E   E
   To You, O Lord, I   lift up my soul,
          B/E A/E   E
In You I trust, O my God.
             B/E A/E   E
Do not let me   be put to shame,
              B/E   A   Bsus4
Nor let my enemies triumph over me.

Chorus:
E2   E2/D♯   E2/C♯
   No one whose hope is in You
       Bsus4 B
Will ever be put to shame;
E   B/E   A2   Bsus4   B
   That's why my eyes are on You, O Lord.
C♯m   C♯m/B
   Surround me,   defend me,
A♯dim
Oh, how I need You.
A
   To You I lift up my soul,
F♯m7   A/B   B7   [**1.** E   B/E   A/E   E   B/E   A/E]
    To You I lift up my soul.
Coda:
E   B/E   A/E   E
   To You, O Lord,   I lift up my soul. [***Repeat x3***]
       B/E   A/E   E
   To You, my Lord,   I lift up my soul.

Verse 2:
E   B/E   A/E   E
   Show me Your ways and   teach me Your paths,
              B/E   A/E   E
Guide me in truth, lead me on;
                 B/E A/E   E
For You're my God,   You are my Saviour,
             B/E   A   Bsus4
My hope is in You each moment of the day.

Verse 3:
E   B/E   A/E   E
   Remember, Lord, Your   mercy and love
           B/E A/E   E
That ever flow from of old.
             B/E   A/E   E
Remember not the sins of my youth,
           B/E   A2/E
Or my rebellious ways.
                        A   E
According to Your love, remember me,
                        A
According to Your love,
F♯m7   B7sus4   B7   B7sus4   B7
For You are good, O Lord

This song is recorded on the Spring Harvest 'No-one Like You - iScape 2006' album

78. TO YOUR THRONE WE'RE WELCOME NOW

(The cross is still speaking today)

Ben Jones

Verse 1:

Bm   G
      To Your throne we're welcome now,
                          D   F♯7
By a new and living way,   new living way.
Bm   G
      Humbled, we draw near to You,
                                   D   F♯7
Broken, but You make us whole,   You make us whole.

Chorus:

Bm   G
The cross is still speaking today,
                                    D
The cross is still making a way
   F♯7   Bm
For us to worship You.
                                   G
Draw near to the most holy place,
                                         D
Draw near with our hearts full of praise,
F♯7   Bm   C♯m/B   F♯7
Now to worship You,
                Bm   [C♯m/B   F♯7]
We worship You.

Verse 2:

Bm   G
      Kingdoms come and kingdoms go,
                         D   F♯7
Riches, desires and flame   will not remain.
Bm   G
      But written in eternity,
                                      D   F♯7
A promise that won't pass away   our debt has been paid.

Tag:

              Bm
You're the Lord of this life, You're the King of this heart,
         G   D
You're everything I could want, all I desire; You are Lord,
      F♯7
You are Lord. [***Repeat***]

This song is recorded on the Spring Harvest 'Glory - New Songs 2010' album

WE BOW OUR HEARTS 79.

(Adoration)

Brenton Brown

Verse 1:
    G   D
We bow our hearts, we lift our hands,
    Em7   C
We turn our eyes to You again,
     G   D
And we surrender to the truth
     Em7   C
That all we need is found in You.

Chorus:
              G   D
Receive our adoration,
         Em7   C
Jesus, Lamb of God.
                G   D
Receive our adoration;
              Em   Em7
How wonderful You are.

Verse 2:
    G   D
We choose to leave it all behind
     Em7   C
And turn our eyes towards the prize.
    G   D
The upward call of God in Christ;
     Em7   C
You have our hearts, Lord; take our lives.

Mid section:
C   D
Every soul You've saved sings out.
                   C   G
Every thing You've made resounds.
               D   C
All creation's standing now, lifting up Your name.
                      D
We're caught up in the angel's song.
                      C   G
We're gathered to Your ancient throne.
                D   C
Children in our Father's arms, shouting out Your praise.

This song is recorded on the Spring Harvest 'Perfect Sacrifice - New Songs 2009' album

80. WE SING A SONG OF SAVING GRACE

(Saving grace)

Neil Bennets
& Eoghan Heaslip

Verse 1:

```
A      D                 E/G♯          A    D                E/G♯
   We sing a song of saving grace    of our Redeemer.
A      D                 E/G♯                A         D                E/G♯
   We sing a song of love's true reign    that's found in Jesus.
```

Bridge:

```
                        D                            F♯m
Be exalted, O God,    on the praises that we bring;
                         Bm
Let every heart now come and worship.
```

Chorus:

```
 A                                  E/G♯
Praise, praise, praise, lift your hands to heaven,
              D                A/C♯          F♯m                    E
For His love has rescued us       from the shadow of the grave.
A                                  E/G♯
Praise, praise, praise to our God for ever,
             D                    A/C♯       D            E/G♯       [1. A       E/G♯   A    E/G♯] [2.  D]
For the glory of His Name,     we sing the song     of saving grace.
```

Verse 2:

```
A        D                E/G♯               A       D                E/G♯
   Your hope in us, it shines the way;    You bring us freedom.
A      D             E/G♯           A          D              E/G♯
   For all our sin and all our shame     You have forgiven.
```

Mid section:

```
D                            A/C♯               F♯m
A love stronger than death has lifted our heads;
                E                                D
And we find peace in the presence of God.
                             A/C♯              D
Love higher than mountains still is the reason we sing,
       A/C♯                 D2
The reason we love You.
```

Chorus:

```
 A                                  E/G♯
Praise, praise, praise, lift your hands to heaven,
              D                A/C♯          F♯m                    E
For His love has rescued us       from the shadow of the grave.
A                                  E/G♯
Praise, praise, praise to our God for ever,
             D                    A/C♯       D            E/G♯          A        E/G♯    [A    E/G♯ x3.]   A
For the glory of His Name,     we sing the song     of saving grace.
```

WE GIVE GLORY AND PRAISE 81.

Matt Osgood

Verse 1:

```
          D                          A
We give glory and praise to the Father;
      F#m                E
Uncreated, immortal, invisible God.
        D                          A
His hands hold the whole of creation,
            F#m                          E
And his heart overflows with love.
```

Verse 2:

```
          D                          A
We give glory and praise to our Saviour;
           F#m                           E
Son of God, Son of Man, perfect payment for sin.
      D                           A
He rose from the grave, he ascended,
            F#m                   Esus4
And one day he will come again.
```

Chorus:

```
   E  D         A
You are so holy, holy, holy,
F#m                E
   The awesome trinity.
D            A                Esus4   E
   Forever Father, Spirit, Son.
A/C#   D                  A
You are, You were and always will be
F#m           E
   God from eternity;
D            A               Esus4    E
   Forever three, forever one.
```

[**1.**]

```
                     D    A
You are our God,
                   Esus4    E
You are our God.
```

Coda:

```
E                    D    A
   You are our God,
                   E
You are our God. [Repeat]

You are our God.
```

Verse 3:

```
          D                          A
We give glory and praise to the Spirit
          F#m                      E
Who inspires and equips us to follow the Son.
        D                             A
Our Helper, our Councel, our Comfort,
       F#m                  Esus4   E
Guarantee of all that's to come.
```

Mid section:

```
E                   Bm7   A/C#                  D2    E
You are our God,              You are our God.
                    Bm7   A/C#                  D2    E
You are our God,              You are our God.
                Bm7        A/C#                  D2
The only God,          You are, the living God,
      E                  D/F#
You are,  Almighty God,
      E/G#             D2       E
You are, You are our God.
```

82. WE WAIT IN HOPE FOR YOU

(Unfailing love)

Nigel Briggs, Rich Bull,
Matt Loose & Phil Squires

Capo 4

Verse:

```
    G                          C/G
We wait in hope for You, our shelter and our truth.
G                             C/G
You are always faithful to Your Word.
    G                                         C/G
Consume our hearts and minds, and be the author of this life.
     G                                C/G
Your kingdom come, Your will be done.
G                                 C
In these times of doubt and sorrow, people need a hope to cling to.
G/B                             C
Your love is an anchor in the storms of life, forever faithful.
```

Chorus:

```
    G          C
    Unfailing love,
                  G/B
    You never let us down.
                  [1. Am7]  [2. Am   C   Em]
    Your promise is alive.
```

Mid section:

```
             G/B          C              Em
When coloured dreams fade to grey unfailing love.
          G/B                C               Em
When the night crowds out the day, unfailing love.
            G/B          C
When there's no words left to say
Em     G/B   Am
  God's love remains.
```

Last chorus:

```
    G          C
    Unfailing love,
                  G/B
    You never let us down.
                  Am7   C   G
    Your promise is alive.
```

This song is recorded on the Spring Harvest 'Acoustic Worship' album

WE WERE LOST
(Pardoned)

83.

Capo 4

Mike Sandeman

Verse 1:

```
Em9              Csus2               Em9             Csus2
   We were lost,         far from God,     enemies of heaven.
Em9                  Csus2
   We were cursed,          condemned to die,
   Am7
But at the cross,
```

Bridge:

```
      Em      D/F#      G                G/D  D
The sinless One was made to be sin for  us;
G/B          C         G/D                    D
We've been given the righteousness of Jesus.
```

Chorus:

```
G                  Am/G   D/G         G
   Pardoned and secure,       in the Father's love,
           Am/G            Dsus4    D
Seated in the heavenly realms.
G              Am/G       D/G             Em
   Reconciled to God,         we're forgiven,
G                Am/G         Dsus4   D
   Never bound by sin again.

G/B          C            G/D                             D
Praise the King who saved us through His suffering,
G/B      C          G/D                      D
For His life was poured out as an offering.  [2. Csus2   D   Csus2   D]
```

Verse 2:

```
Em9               Csus2                  Em9                       Csus2
   Dividing walls,       now destroyed,         and wrath that stood against us,
Em9              Csus2
   Christ the man       drank that cup
   Am7
As through the cross . . .
```
Bridge - Chorus 1 - Chorus 2:

Chorus 2:

```
G              Am/G   D/G              G
   See the glory,           sense the majesty,
               Am/G     Dsus4    D
Know the mystery of God.
G          Am/G  D/G             Em
   Revelation          of his wisdom,
G                Am/G      [Dsus4   D]  [Coda: Dsus4   D   Dsus4   D   G2]
   Shown to us in Jesus Christ.
G/B
Praise the . . .
```

Mid section:

```
Csus2             D
All my sins are washed away.
Csus2                        D                       [C/G   D/F#]
Through Your death, the price You paid. [x3]
```

84. WE WILL DANCE

(For your glory)

Ben Cantelon
& Matt Redman

Capo 2

Verse 1:

                A
We will dance,   we will dance for Your glory,

We will dance, we will dance for Your glory,
                G   D/F♯   A
We will dance   for Your glory, Lord.

Verse 2:

We will lift up a shout to adore You,

Every sound that we make, it is for You,
                G   D/F♯   A
We will dance   for Your glory, Lord.

Bridge:

          G
For salvation's in this place,
             D/F♯
You're the name by which we're saved:
        A
Jesus,   Jesus.
             G
Let Your name be lifted high,
             D/F♯
As our thankful hearts now cry:
     F♯m   G
'Jesus,   Jesus'.

Chorus:

  A
Lift up your heads, you ancient gates.
 F♯m7
Be lifted up, you ancient doors:
    G   D
The King is coming in, the King is coming in.
     A
We lift up a shout shake the skies.
 F♯m7
Lift up a cry: 'be glorified!'
    G   D
The King is coming in, the King is coming in.

Mid Section:

          A
We're the people of God with a song to sing,

And we're bringing our lives as an offering;
         G   D   A
We will dance for Your glory, Lord.
          A
And Your cross is the hope that we hold up high,

As we tell the whole world of Your love and life;
         G   D   A
We will dance for Your glory, Lord.

WE, YOUR CHILDREN, PRAY LORD 85.

(King of the broken)

Paul Baloche, Steven Curtis-Chapman, Stuart Garrard,
Israel Houghton, Tim Hughes, Graham Kendrick,
Andy Park, Matt Redman, Martin Smith,
Michael W. Smith, Chris Tomlin, Darlene Zschech

Capo 1

Verse 1:

```
G                     Gsus4 G
We, Your children, pray     Lord,
                             Gsus4    G
Humbly seek Your face;
Em7                  D/C C
We turn from our sin,   Lord,
        G                D
You hear us as we pray.
```

Verse 2:

```
G                   Gsus4 G
Healing King of na  -  tions,
                           Gsus4    G
Let your kingdom come.
Em7                  D/C C
Purify your church,     Lord,
        G            D
Your Glory over us.
```

Bridge:

```
C               G/B
Heal us, forgive us,
    D                        Em7
Restore our hearts again.
C        D
Fill us, breathe upon us.
```

Chorus:

```
Gsus4  G   D/F#  Em7
Je  -  sus, Jesus, Healer of nations,
C
Hope of salvation.
Gsus4  G   Bm7   Em7
Je  -  sus, Jesus, King of our hearts,
C                       [1. G   Gsus4  G    Gsus4  G]
King of  the broken.   [2. Am G        C    Em7    D    Am    G   C   D/C    C]
                        [Last time:    G]
```

Verse 3:

```
G                 Gsus4 G
Lover of the woun  -  ded,
                       Gsus4    G
Defender of the weak,
Em7                  D/C C
Friend of the forgot  -  ten;
        G                D
You wipe away our tears.
```

86. WELCOME, YOU ARE WELCOME
(Inhabit the praise)

Vicky Beeching

Capo 3

Verse 1:

C   F/C
Welcome, You are welcome;
   C   Gsus4/C
See Your people drawing near.
      C   F/C
Overwhelm us with Your presence;
     C   F
Lord, reveal your glory here.

Bridge:

            Dm
We are singing and bringing
       C/E   F
You love songs with our hands held high.

Chorus:

G   Am   F   C/E   G Am
Oh,   inhabit the praise of Your people,
   F   C/E   G   Am
Inhabit this place as we seek You.
F   C/E   G   F
Visit us, Lord, You're the one we're longing for,
              G   F   [G   Am   F   C/E   G   Am   F   C/E]
Jesus, You're the one we're longing for.   [***last x*** C]

Verse 2:

C   F/C
Gazing at Your beauty, Lord,
   C   Gsus4/C
You face will make us new.
      C   F/C
Thirsty for your whispers,
     C   F
Chasing after more of You.

Mid section:

            C
Let his praises rise, let his praises rise. [***x2***]
            C   G/B   Am   F
Let his praises rise, let his praises rise. [***x4***]

WELL, JESUS IS THE ROCK
(Lead me to the rock)

87.

Brian Houston

Capo 1(D)

Verse 1:

       D   G   D   E   D
Well, Jesus is the Rock of my salvation: so lead me to the Rock that is higher than I.
                          G   D   E   D
And he is my fortress so I will not be shaken: lead me to the Rock that is higher than I.
                      G   D   E   D
My soul finds rest in God alone: lead me to the Rock that is higher than I.
                               G   D   E   D
And he is the place where my hope comes from: lead me to the Rock that is higher than I.

Chorus:

G
Lead me to the One who is strong and sure,
F
Lead me to the One who gives me strength to endure.
E
Lead me to the One who teaches me his ways,
      A
And lead me to the One who loves the sounds of my praise.

Verse 2:

 D   G   D   E   D
Trust in the Lord every day of Your life, and lead me to the Rock that is higher than I.
                            G   D   E   D
And into his arms you can run and hide: lead me to the Rock that is higher than I.
                                G   D   E   D
One thing he has spoken, two things I have heard: lead me to the Rock that is higher than I.
                                         G   D   E   D
From his strength and his love he gives great rewards: lead me to the Rock that is higher than I.

Verse 3:

         D   G   D   E   D
For my soul finds rest in God alone: lead me to the Rock that is higher than I.
                             G   D   E   D
And he is the place that my hope comes from: lead me to the Rock that is higher than I.
                           G   D   E   D
So trust in the Lord every day of your life: lead me to the Rock that is higher than I.
                                           G D   A7   D
 And into his arms You can run and hide: lead me to the Rock that is higher than I.

This song is recorded on the Spring Harvest 'Glory - New Songs 2010' album

88. WHAT A MORNING

(Christ is risen indeed)

Matt Boswell

Verse 1:

A D
What a morning when the silence turned to singing;
A D
What rejoicing on that third appointed day.
F♯m7 D
The cross exhausted all its cruelty and its power,
Bm D E
But love declared its victory, rolled the stone away.

Chorus:

A F♯m7
Christ is risen,
E D
He is risen indeed;
E D
Death has been defeated and the grave
E
Has lost its sting.
A F♯m7
Hallelujah,
E D
With the angels we will sing:
Bm D
Christ is risen,
E A [Dsus2/A] [***End*** A]
Christ is risen indeed.

Verse 2:

A D
Such a hope we have in Christ the resurrection;
A D
Such a joy to know by grace we've been redeemed.
F♯m7 D
Through Christ we died a death to sin and all its folly;
Bm D E
Glorified, we will rise, to live eternally.

Mid section:

D A/C♯ Bm A/C♯
Salvation and immortal praise to our victorious King;
D A/C♯ Bm A/C♯ D
Let the heavens and the earth with glad hosannas ring.

This song is recorded on the Spring Harvest 'Glory - New Songs 2010' album

WHEN THE SUN IS SHINING

(Jesus is my best friend)

89.

Vicky Beeching
& Wendy Beech-Ward

Verse 1:

```
A                    E A                      E
When the sun is shining, and I go out to play,
A                  E A                    E
I'm so glad that Jesus walks with me all day.
```

Chorus:

```
D              E F#m
Jesus is my best friend,
D              E F#m
Jesus is my best friend;
D                E F#m  D
We will be together forever and ever,
   E         F#m
Forever and ever.
     D       E  F#m
Sing: ah, oh (ah,      oh)
D        E  F#m
Ah, oh (ah,        oh.)
     D       E  F#m
Sing ah, oh (ah,       oh.)
     D       E  F#m        [Last x  Dsus2]
Sing ah, oh (ah,       oh.)
```

Verse 2:.

```
A                    E A                      E
When I'm feeling lonely, when I start to cry,
A                E A                        E
I hear Jesus whisper that he's right by my side.
```

Verse 3:

```
A                         E A                              E
When I leave Spring Harvest, and sometimes life is tough,
A                         E A                        E
I know You're still with me, and Your love is enough.
```

Mid section:

```
D        E
  Jesus,     I love You.
F#m      E/G#
  Jesus,     I love You.  [Repeat]
```

This song is recorded on the Spring Harvest 'Journey - Live Worship 2009' album

90. WHO IS LIKE THE LORD OUR GOD

(To the praise of Your glory)

Ben Hall
& Nathan Fellingham

Capo 2

Verse 1:

G   Bm   D
   Who is like the Lord our God,
G   Bm   D
   Reigning high above the earth?
G   Bm   D
   Sovereign over everything,
G   Bm   D
   Holding all the universe.

Bridge:

              Bm
So we will bow in awe,
                Gm6
Turning our hearts to Yours.

Chorus:

               D   Em7   Bm   A
To the praise of Your glory we live,   we breathe;
        D   Em7   Bm   A
Testifying to You and the life   You give.
             Bm   A/C♯   D
We now set our hope on Christ,
             G   A   Bm
Laying earthly things aside.
                 D   A   [**1.** G   Bm   D] [**2.** D   Em7   Bm   Asus4   A **x2**] [**3.4.** G]
We were dead, but You've made us alive.

Verse 2:

G   Bm   D
   While creating sea and land,
G   Bm   D
   Throwing stars into the sky,
G   Bm   D
   Carving mountains with his hands;
G   Bm   D
   In his mind were you and I.

WHO, O LORD, COULD SAVE THEMSELVES 91.

(You alone can rescue)

Matt Redman
& Jonas Myrin

__Capo 4__

Verse 1:
G   C   G
Who, O Lord, could save themselves,
C   Dsus4   D
Their own soul could heal?
    Em   G/B   C   G
Our shame was deeper than the sea;
      C   Dsus4 D G
Your grace is deep - er still. [***Repeat***]

Chorus:
                    C
And You alone can rescue,
D   Em
You alone can save.
               C   D   Em
You alone can lift us from the grave.
                   C   D   Em
You came down to find us, led us out of death.
               C   D   Gsus4   G   Gsus4   G
[**1.**]   To You alone belongs the highest praise.
               C   D   Em
[**2.**]   To You alone belongs the highest praise.
               C   D   Em
To You alone belongs the highest praise.
               C   D   Gsus4   G   Gsus4   G   Gsus4   G   Gsus4   G
To You alone belongs the highest praise.

Verse 2:
G   C   G
You, O Lord, have made a way,
    C   Dsus4   D
The great divide You healed;
    Em   G/B   C   G
For when our hearts were far away,
      C   Dsus4 D   G
Your love went fur   -   ther still.
           C   D   G
Yes, Your love goes further still!

Mid section:
    G   C
We lift up our eyes, lift up our eyes, You're the giver of life. [***Repeat***]
    Em   C
We lift up our eyes, lift up our eyes, You're the giver of life. [***Repeat***]

92. YOU ALONE ARE WORTHY

(Glory in the highest)

Al Gordon, Luke Hellebronth
& Hanif Williams

Capo 2

Verse 1:

```
C                   G/B
   You alone are worthy,
Am7             F                      C
   You alone deserve the highest praise.
                    G/B
We bow down to worship,
Am7                  F                    C
   We bow down to seek You in this place.
```

Chorus:

```
          G                    Am
We sing glory, glory in the highest,
            F                   C    [2. G/B   Am7   F]
Glory in the highest, glory to our God. [4. C/E]
```

Verse 2:

```
C                      G/B
   For Your love and mercy,
Am7              F                  C
   For the beauty of Your saving grace;
                     G/B
We have come to thankYou.
Am7                  F               C
   We have come to worship You today.
```

Mid section:

```
    G       F
As we bow down,
    G    F
Be lifted high.
    G       F
As we bow down,
    G    Fmaj7   F
Be lifted high.
```

This song is recorded on the Spring Harvest 'Journey - Live Worship 2009' album

YOU ARE MY STRENGTH

Reuben Morgan

Verse 1:

```
              G                            C2
You are my strength, strength like no other,
                 G/B  D              G
Strength like no other    reaches to me.
```

Verse 2:

```
             G                      C2
You are my hope,  hope like no other,
             G/B  D              G
Hope like no other    reaches to me.
```

Chorus:

```
         C2
In the fullness of Your grace,
         Em7
In the power of Your name
          D/F♯ G   C2
You lift me up,
            D
You lift me up.
```

Verse 3:

```
         G                    C2
Unfailing love stronger than mountains,
             G/B    D            G
Deeper than oceans    reaches to me.
```

Mid section:

```
C      G         D  Em7          C        G   D   Em7
   Your love, O Lord, reaches to the heavens,
C      G         D  Em7       C       G   D   Em7
   Your faithfulness    reaches to the skies.
C      G         D  Em7          C        G   D   Em7
   Your love, O Lord, reaches to the heavens,
C      G         D  Em7       C       G   D
   Your faithfulness    reaches to the skies.
```

Verse 1:

```
              G                            C2
You are my strength, strength like no other,
                 G/B  D              G
Strength like no other    reaches to me.
```

94. YOU ARE THE REASON

(God of all)

Ben Cantelon
& Robin Hardingham

```
Verse 1:
               C2                   G       D
You are the reason why I am here today.
              C2                 G             D
You are the reason why I sing Your praise.
            C2             G                 D
You are creator of the heavens and earth.
         C                 Em        D/F♯
So we join with angels and proclaim:

     Chorus:
              Em        C    G    D
     You are God of all creation,
               Em    C           G       D
     And the stars above sing alleluia,
             C        Em        Bm              C
     And together as one voice we declare:
          D  [1. Em   C   D/G   Em/A]  [2. Em  D  C  x4]
     You are God.

Verse 2:
           C2                  G        D
You are forever strong and mighty,
           C2             G        D
You are eternal King of majesty.
              C2                  G        D
Even the mountains and the seas below
            C             Em       D/F♯
Cry out: 'Holy is the Lord of all'.

Mid section:
C2                      D
Glory, glory in the highest.
C2                      D
Glory, glory in the highest.
C                       D
Glory, glory in the highest.
Em                      D/F♯
Glory, glory in the highest.

You are . . .

     Last chorus:
              Em        C    G    D
     You are God of all creation,
               Em    C           G       D
     And the stars above sing alleluia,
             C        Em        Bm              C
     And together as one voice we declare:
     Cmaj7        D   Em
             You are God.
```

YOU CAME TO SAVE THE WORLD
(Third day)

<u>**Capo 3**</u>

Simon Brading
& Matt Redman

Verse 1:

```
    G
You came to save the world, to redeem creation;
Bm                                              Asus4   A
Faced up to the cross, You carried every sin on Your shoulders.
    G
The crowd, they didn't know, on the cross You conquered;
Bm                                                         Asus4    A
As You breathed Your last, You knew that "It was finished", but not over.
```

Bridge:

```
          Em                      Bm
For three days, You laid in that grave,
    G                              A
But death was swallowed up in victory.
```

Chorus:

```
           D            A
For You arose on the third   day:
      Em7             G
'Hallelujah!' we cry, Your life is our life.
         D                  A
Yes, You arose You on the third   day;
        Em7          G                           D/A   A   [1. G   D]
We are fully alive, in the power of Your life, You're alive.
```

Verse 2:

```
G
Just as You arose,  bursting out in power,
Bm                                             Asus4  A
We are raised to life,  reigning with You now and forever.
G
Just as You returned,  to the Father's glory,
Bm                                          Asus4    A
 I've been made his child;  living to enjoy You forever.
```

Mid section

```
    G                                D
You overcame, You overcame at the cross.
    G                                 Bm7
You rose again, You rose again, raising us.
```

Coda:

```
G                           D/A   A   D
Power of Your life, You're alive.
```

96. YOU CAME TO US, THE SERVANT KING

(Great is our God)

<u>**Capo 1**</u>

Cathy and Paul Burton
& Jim Elliot

Verse:

```
Em7                         G
   You came to us, the Servant King,
D                      A(no3rd)
   Eternal life the offering;
Em7                           G                    D     A(no3rd)
   You took my sin and shame and made a way.
Em7                     G
   Captured by Your love and grace,
D                     A(no3rd)
   Now we live to seek Your face,
Em7                                G                    D      A(no3rd)
   And show the world Your power and Your mercy.
```

Bridge:

```
C
   What an awesome God,
D
   What amazing love,
C                                D
   And for ever we will sing.
```

Chorus:

```
                Em7      G
Great is our God,   hallelujah,
D                       A(no3rd)            Em7
   Great is our God,   He will not fail,
       G             D       A(no3rd)
His love will never  fail.
                Em7                 G
Great is our God,    strong and mighty,
D     A(no3rd)        Em7
   King for ever more,
        G                 D   A(no3rd)   [1x only Em7    G     D     A(no3rd)]
He reigns for ever more,          (Yeah.)
```

Last time:

```
                 Em7    D    Asus2/C♯    C6
Great is our God.
                 Em7    D    Asus2/C♯    Cmaj7
Great is our God.
```

YOU PAINT THE NIGHT
(God, You reign)

Lincoln Brewster
& Mia Fieldes

Verse 1:
```
D                        G/D
   You paint the night,
D                      G/D                        Bm
   You count the stars and You call them by name;
                  D                   D    G/D
The skies proclaim: God, You reign.
D                     G/D
   Your glory shines,
D                G/D                          Bm
  You teach the sun when to bring a new day;
              G                     D
Creation sings: God, You reign.
```

Chorus:
```
           G                   Bm
God You reign, God You reign,
               A7sus4     G
Forever and ever,
           D
God You reign.  (Whoa, God You . . .)
```

Verse 2:
```
D                    G/D
   You part the seas,
D                      G/D                               Bm
   You move the mountains with the words that You say;
                    G                D      G/D
My song remains: God, You reign.
D                    G/D
   You hold my life,
D                      G/D                      Bm
   You know my heart and You call me by name;
            G                  D
I live to say: God, You reign.
```

Mid section:
```
    A/C♯ Em  D   Bm  A/C♯ D
Hal - le - lu - jah, hal  -  le - lu.
    A/C♯ Em  D   Bm   A   D
Hal - le - lu - jah, hal - le - lu.
    A/C♯  G/B D/A   G    A    D
Hal - le  -  lu - jah,   hal - le - lu.
    A/C♯  G/B D/A  Em7 A   D
Hal - le  -  lu - jah,   hal - le - lu.   God You . . .
```

98. YOU FIND ME WITH ONE GLANCE

(Glorious life)

Lyrics: Nigel Briggs
Music: Trent

Verse 1:

```
      Bm                      G2
You find me with one glance,
Bm
Led me out of darkness,
G2
Washed away my past.
     Bm                 G2
Forgiven now I stand;
       Bm
With You there is a promise
    G2
Of hope that always lasts.
```

Bridge:

```
A                               Bm
   You're the reason I get down on my knees
A                            Em          G
   And the reason my heart sings Your praise.
```

Chorus:

```
D
   Through grace You've given liberty.
Asus4
   Your mercy flowing over me
Bm                    G
   From darkness into glorious life.
D
    Your hand has come to rescue me
Asus4
   And showed me who I'm meant to be;
Bm                  G         [Last x Bm   D   G   Bm   D   G   Bm]
   In Jesus there is glorious life.
```

Verse 2:

```
        Bm                 G2
You're with me as I wake,
  Bm
I leave my bed to follow You,
G2
Face another day.
       Bm                 G2
With You there is no hate.
       Bm
Your love it does a better job,
G2
Shows a better way.
```

This song is recorded on the Spring Harvest 'Glory - New Songs 2010' album

YOU SEE ALL THINGS

(Love divine)

99.

Lyrics: Nigel Briggs
Music: Trent

Verse:

```
Bm                              A/B
You see all things, into the corners of each heart;
G/B                                         F#sus4          F#/A#
Everything is in Your hands from the cradles to the stars.
Bm                        A/B
You take our dreams, and all we hope to be;
          G/B                                  F#sus4                  F#/A#
Through joy and tears, pain and laughter, we know You'll never leave.
```

Chorus:

```
Bm               A
Oh, You are a love divine;
       F#m
There's nothing better in this world
    G                Em
That we could ever find.
Bm       A
Oh, Your truth gives life;
    F#m
You came to set the captives free
             G                Em   [1. Bm   A/B   G   F#sus4/C#   F#/A#]
And You've opened up our eyes.     [2. G]
```

Mid section:

```
                                   A
We were lost, now we're found,
                              G
Changed inside and out
                                   A   Bm   A2   G   F#   F#/A#
When Your love came down.
```

Chorus:

```
Bm               A
Oh, You are a love divine;
       F#m
There's nothing better in this world
    G                Em
That we could ever find.
Bm       A
Oh, Your truth gives life;
    F#m
You came to set the captives free
             G                Em
And You've opened up our eyes.
```

Coda:

```
G     A                              G      A       Bm
          You've opened up our lives,          oh.
```

100. YOUR GRACE IS ENOUGH

(This is our God)

Reuben Morgan

<u>**Capo 4**</u>

Verse 1:

```
C                      Em                    Am
   Your grace is enough, more than I need.
         F
At Your word, I will believe.
C                 Em                Am
   I wait for You, draw near again.
                  F                     G
   Let Your Spirit make me new.
```

Chorus:

```
                C/E               F
And I will fall at Your feet.
         Dm            G/B
I will fall at Your feet.
                C/E               F  [2. C   G   Dm   Am   F   C]
And I will worship You here.
```

Verse 2:

```
C                      Em                     Am
   Your presence in me,  Jesus, light the way
           F
By the power of Your word.
C                 Em                Am
   I am restored,   I am redeemed.
                  F                G
   By Your Spirit, I am free.
```

Mid section:

```
                   C
Freely You gave it all for us.
                          G
Surrendered Your life upon that cross.
                  Dm                  Am
Great is the love poured out for all.
       F          C
This is our God.
                 C
Lifted on high from death to life.
                   G
Forever our God is glorified.
                    Dm                Am
Servant and King rescued the world.
       F            C
This is our God.
```

This song is recorded on the Spring Harvest 'Glory - New Songs 2010' album

GUITAR CHORDS

A good chord vocabulary is essential for a guitarist to feel confident when playing in worship, especially when the situation may involve reading a previously unseen piece of music or picking up a song quickly by ear. The chords on these pages are arranged in 'families' according to key. This is a beneficial way of remembering chords as most songs stick to these groupings. For each key, the first row shows the simplest form of each chord and the second line gives a more interesting substitution. The third line shows the chords most commonly used by guitarists derived by keeping some sort of pedal tone ringing in each chord and the fourth line shows inverted chords with an alternate bass note.

Also included are the Roman Numerals and Nashville Numbers associated with each chord. If you've not come across these before, they are simply an easy way of numbering each chord within a key. This is useful as it means you can take any chord progression in one key and instantly transpose it to another. Furthermore you can try out any of the chords in each column that corresponds to the relevant Roman Numeral and see if there is chord type or inversion which still fits but adds a different flavour. Experimentation like this may open up creative chord progressions that serve as a catalyst to help you to worship in fresh ways or to write new songs.

	Roman	I	II	III	IV	V	VI	VII
	Nashville	1	2	3	4	5	6	7
Key of C	3-note chord (triad)	C 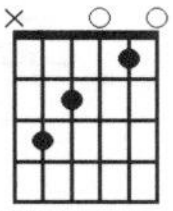	Dm 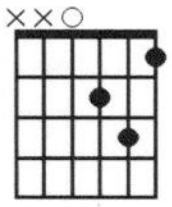	Em 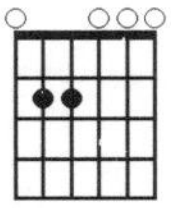	F 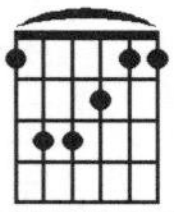	G 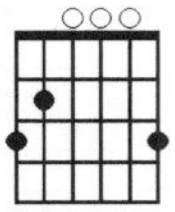	Am 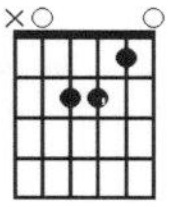	Bdim 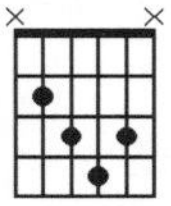
	4-note chord	Cmaj7 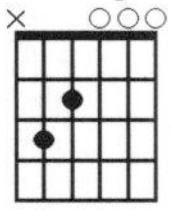	Dm7 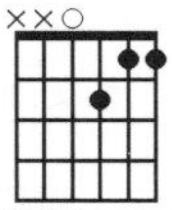	Em7 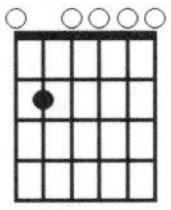	Fmaj7 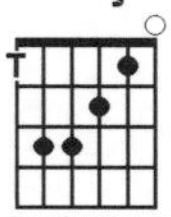	G7 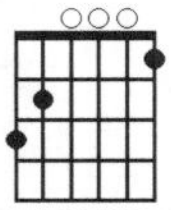	Am7 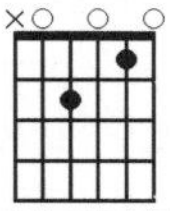	Bm7♭5 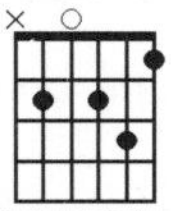
	Alternative substitute	C 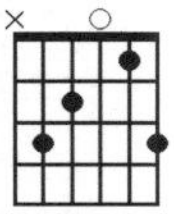	D7sus4 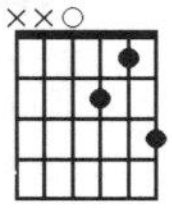	Em7 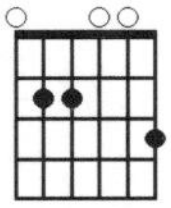	Fsus2 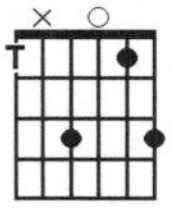	G5 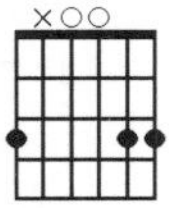	Am7 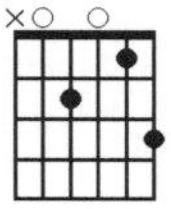	Dsus4/B 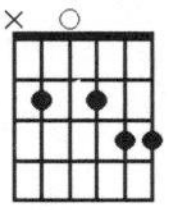
	Alternative bass note	C/E 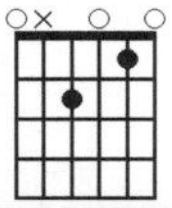	Dm/F 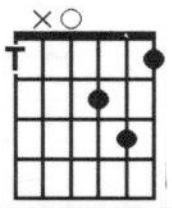	Em/G 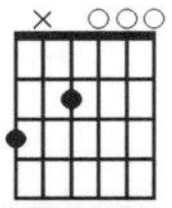	F/A 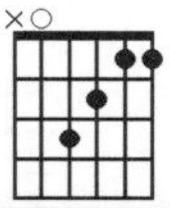	F/G 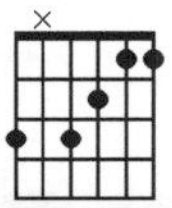	Am/E 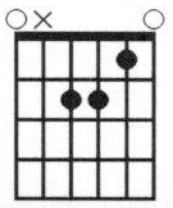	

For all chords in the key of C# or Db, use the chords from the key of C with capo 1

More Chord Charts Overleaf

GUITAR CHORDS

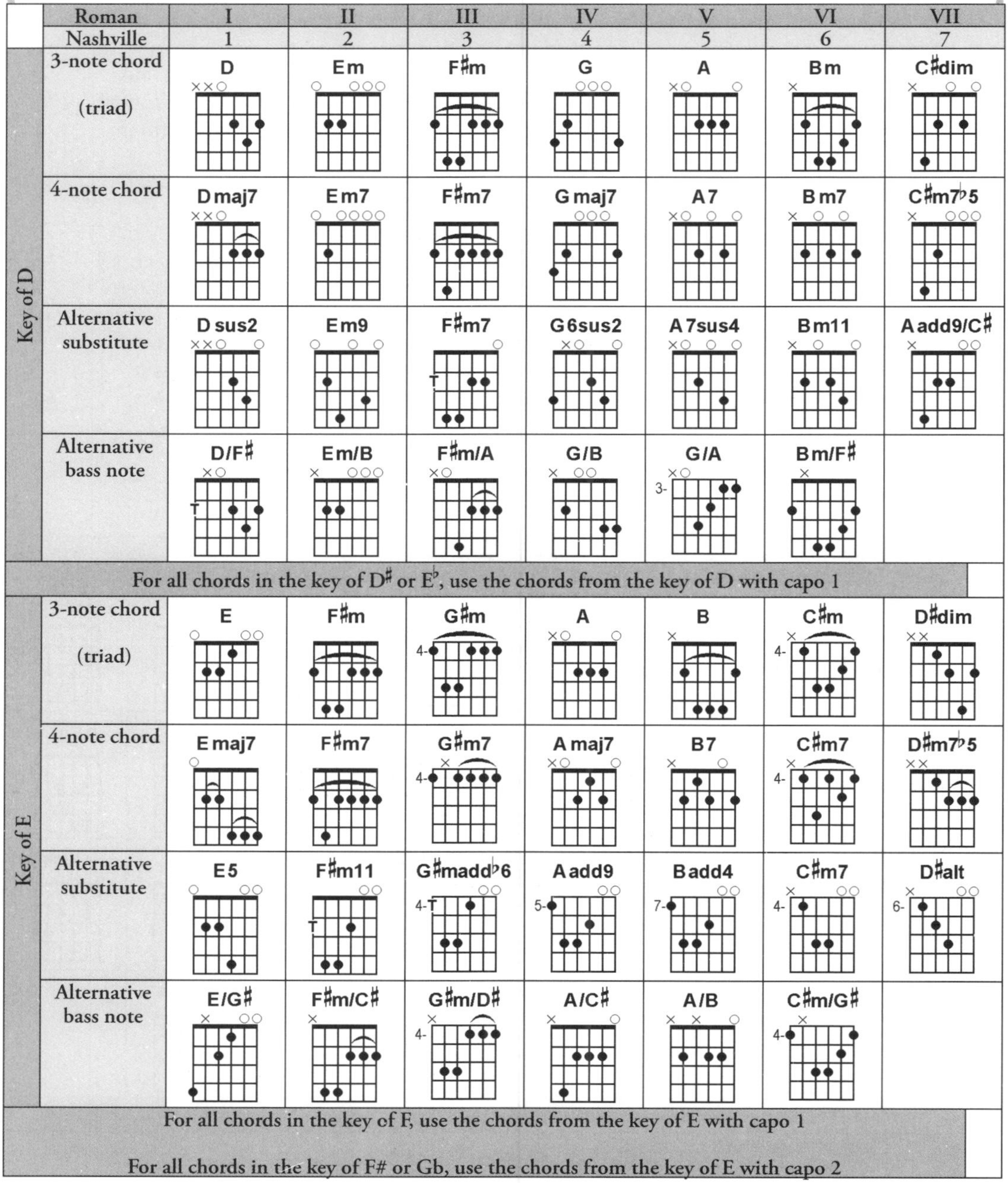

	Roman	I	II	III	IV	V	VI	VII
	Nashville	1	2	3	4	5	6	7
Key of D	3-note chord (triad)	D	Em	F♯m	G	A	Bm	C♯dim
Key of D	4-note chord	Dmaj7	Em7	F♯m7	Gmaj7	A7	Bm7	C♯m7♭5
Key of D	Alternative substitute	Dsus2	Em9	F♯m7	G6sus2	A7sus4	Bm11	Aadd9/C♯
Key of D	Alternative bass note	D/F♯	Em/B	F♯m/A	G/B	G/A	Bm/F♯	
For all chords in the key of D♯ or E♭, use the chords from the key of D with capo 1								
Key of E	3-note chord (triad)	E	F♯m	G♯m	A	B	C♯m	D♯dim
Key of E	4-note chord	Emaj7	F♯m7	G♯m7	Amaj7	B7	C♯m7	D♯m7♭5
Key of E	Alternative substitute	E5	F♯m11	G♯madd♭6	Aadd9	Badd4	C♯m7	D♯alt
Key of E	Alternative bass note	E/G♯	F♯m/C♯	G♯m/D♯	A/C♯	A/B	C♯m/G♯	
For all chords in the key of F, use the chords from the key of E with capo 1 For all chords in the key of F# or Gb, use the chords from the key of E with capo 2								

GUITAR CHORDS

	Roman	I	II	III	IV	V	VI	VII
	Nashville	1	2	3	4	5	6	7
Key of G	3-note chord (triad)	G	Am	Bm	C	D	Em	F♯dim
Key of G	4-note chord	G maj7	Am7	Bm7	C maj7	D7	Em7	F♯m7♭5
Key of G	Alternative substitute	G	A7sus4	Dsus4/B	Cadd9	Dsus4	Em7	G/F♯
Key of G	Alternative bass note	G/D	Am/C	Bm/D	C/G	C/D	Em/G	
	For all chords in the key of G♯ or A♭, use the chords from the key of G with capo 1							
Key of A	3-note chord (Triad)	A	Bm	C♯m	D	E	F♯m	G♯dim
Key of A	4-note chord	A maj7	Bm7	C♯m7	D maj7	E7	F♯m7	G♯m7♭5
Key of A	Alternative substitute	A sus2	Bsus4	C♯m7	D6sus2	Eadd9	F♯m11	Eadd9/G♯
Key of A	Alternative bass note	A/E	Bm/F♯	C♯m/E	D/A	D/E	F♯m/A	

For all chords in the key of A# or Bb, use the chords from the key of A with capo 1

For all chords in the key of B, use the chords from the key of A with capo 2

SCRIPTURE INDEX

JOHN

ACTS

ROMANS

1 CORINTHIANS

2 CORINTHIANS

GALATIANS

EPHESIANS

PHILIPPIANS

2:5 Meekness and majesty
2:7 You came to us, the servant King
2:8 Have you heard
2:8 This is our song
2:8 You came to save the world
2:9 Look inside the mystery
2:10 All the heavens praise
2:10 I'm not backing down
2:10 You alone are worthy
2:15 There's a new day dawning
2:9-10 Jesus, beautiful Saviour
3:10 Jesus, my passion in life
3:7-11 All I once held dear
14:20 Forever and a day

COLOSSIANS

1:18 Come, see the Son
1:13-16 The God who set the stars in space
2:9 You see all things
2:14 I'll remember You
2:15 At the cross, where Jesus suffered
3:8 God whose voice called worlds

1 THESSALONIANS

4:14 I stand amazed
4:14 You came to save the world
5:10 I stand amazed
5:10 We were lost

2 THESSALONIANS

1:10 Hallelujah

1 TIMOTHY

1:17 Now unto the King who reigns over all
6:15 Before the world was made

2 TIMOTHY

1:10 Oh, how could it be
2:8 I'm casting my cares aside

TITUS

2:11 Your grace is enough
3:7 Your grace is enough

HEBREWS

1:3 Jesus You endured my pain
1:6 Life could take
2:9 I stand amazed
3:12 Life could take
4:13 God whose voice called worlds
5:8 We, Your children, pray Lord
6:5 Jesus, my passion in life
6:18 Now unto the King who reigns over all
9:28 My Lord, what love is this
10:12 My Lord, what love is this
10:19-20 To Your throne we're welcome now
12:2 I will not boast of anything
12:2 Jesus You endured my pain
12:3 I'm casting my cares aside
12:28 Come, learn of God's kingdom
13:8 My God is good
13:15 I'm not backing down

JAMES

1:2 Defender of this heart
5:11 See Martha weeping at a tomb
5:11 There is an everlasting kindness

1 PETER

1:2 May the Lord bless you
1:3 My God is good
1:3 Who is like the Lord our God
1:3 You came to save the world
1:19 Jesus, beautiful Saviour
1:20 Before the world was made
2:9 Come, learn of God's kingdom
2:24 I will cast my cares
2:24 I'll remember You
4:11 It's falling from the clouds
4:12 Gonna dance, dance

2 PETER

1:4 Now unto the King who reigns over all
1:10 Life could take

1 JOHN

1:7 Search my heart
1:9 God whose voice called worlds
2:1 Once I was dead to You
2:17 Breathe on me
3:5 My Lord, what love is this
3:20 A limitless majesty
4:19 All because of You

JUDE

1:21 Love that will not let me go

REVELATION

1:5 He is jealous for me
1:6 Forever and a day
2:9 You find me with one glance
2:16 You find me with one glance
3:9 Your grace is enough
4:8 All the heavens praise
4:8 Here inside Your presence
4:8 Holy, holy is the Lord God Almighty
4:8 You are the reason
4:11 Be lifted high above the heavens
4:11 It's falling from the clouds
5:11 All the heavens praise
5:13 Forever and a day
6:10 We, Your children, pray Lord
7:11 Hope is here
7:12 Forever and a day
7:14 Jesus You endured my pain
7:14 On the dark night
9:14 Life could take
11:15 Creation sings the Father's song
12:11 Jesus You endured my pain
15:3 All the heavens praise
15:4 It's falling from the clouds
15:4 Who, O Lord, could save themselves
15:4 You alone are worthy
19:1 Can you hear, there's a new song
19:1 Creation sings the Father's song
19:1 Hallelujah
19:6 You came to us, the servant King
19:6 You paint the night
19:7 God whose voice called worlds
20:14 The God who set the stars in space
21:2 By faith we see the hand of God
22:20 Welcome, You are welcome

THEMATIC INDEX

HEALING

By this world my heart was wounded
Deliverer, come set me free
Hope is here
Love that will not let me go
My God is good
Once I was dead to You
See Martha weeping at a tomb
There's a new day dawning
You are my strength

HEART WORSHIP

A limitless majesty
All I once held dear
As we come into Your presence
Breathe on me
Defender of this heart
Forever and a day
Hallelujah
I am an instrument of the living God
I will exalt You
I'll remember You
It's falling from the clouds
Jesus, beautiful Saviour
Jesus, my passion in life
Let the words of my mouth
Lord, my life is an empty cup
Meekness and majesty
More than just another song
On the dark night
Open my eyes
To give as You gave
To Your throne we're welcome now
We bow our hearts
Who is like the Lord our God
You alone are worthy
You paint the night

HEAVEN AND THE PROMISE OF ETERNITY

By faith we see the hand of God
Come, learn of God's kingdom
Creation sings the Father's song
Forever and a day
I see Your face
Look inside the mystery
Once I was dead to You
We, Your children, pray Lord

HOLY SPIRIT

Deliverer, come set me free
God whose voice called worlds
I'm not backing down
Search my heart
We give glory and praise
Your grace is enough

JESUS

CROSS AND RESURRECTION

At the cross, where Jesus suffered
Come, see the Son
Creation sings the Father's song
Dark before the dawn
Have you heard
Hope is here
I see Your face
I stand amazed
I will not boast of anything
Jesus You endured my pain
Life could take
Look inside the mystery
Meekness and majesty
My Lord, what love is this
O precious sight
We give glory and praise
We were lost
What a morning
Who, O Lord, could save themselves
You came to save the world

JUSTICE

God whose voice called worlds
I'm not backing down
Now unto the King who reigns over all
The God who set the stars in space
There is an everlasting kindness
To give as You gave
You came to us, the servant King

LIVING FOR GOD

All I once held dear
Behold, a broken world
Break our hearts
God whose voice called worlds
Here inside Your presence
I am an instrument of the living God
I am chosen
I'm casting my cares aside
I'm not backing down
Jesus, my passion in life
Let the words of my mouth
More than just another song
Search my heart
The God who set the stars in space
There is an everlasting kindness
There's a new day dawning
To give as You gave
To You, O Lord
We will dance
Well, Jesus is the rock
When the sun is shining
You came to us, the servant King
You find me with one glance

LOVE AND DEVOTION

A limitless majesty
All because of You
All I once held dear
As we come into Your presence
Break our hearts
Breathe on me
Forever and a day
Hallelujah
Here inside Your presence
How great is Your love
I see Your face
Jesus, beautiful Saviour
Jesus, my passion in life
Life could take
Love that will not let me go
My times are in Your hands
Open my eyes
To give as You gave
We bow our hearts
We will dance
You alone are worthy
You see all things

MERCY, GRACE AND FORGIVENESS

A limitless majesty
At the cross, where Jesus suffered
By this world my heart was wounded
Dark before the dawn
Have you heard
Hope is here
How great is Your love
I stand amazed
I will not boast of anything
Life could take
May the Lord bless you
My Lord, what love is this
Nothing can separate
O precious sight
On the dark night
Once I was dead to You
The God who set the stars in space
There is an everlasting kindness
This is our song
To You, O Lord
To Your throne we're welcome now
We sing a song of saving grace
We were lost
Who, O Lord, could save themselves
You came to us, the servant King
You find me with one glance

MISSION

By faith we see the hand of God
Can you hear, there's a new song
God whose voice called worlds
Have you heard
Hope is here
I'm not backing down
There is an everlasting kindness
There's a new day dawning
This is our song
To give as You gave

MYSTERY/ TRANSCENDENCE AND POWER OF GOD

All the heavens praise
Before the world was made
Creation sings the Father's song
Deliverer, come set me free
Give unto the Lord
God whose voice called worlds
Have you heard
Jesus, beautiful Saviour
Look inside the mystery
There is an everlasting kindness
We give glory and praise
We were lost
Who is like the Lord our God

LITURGY & SPOKEN WORSHIP INDEX

THE WHY, WHAT AND WHEN OF LITURGY

Sue Rinaldi

Why?

I have often heard people ask about the importance of liturgy and how to use the examples from the Spring Harvest songbook. Are they simply meeting-fillers or do they serve a more meaningful and formational role? These questions deserve many pages of exploration - in fact, there are some great books on the subject - but let's give a quick guide.

Over the past few years, an increasing emphasis on 'Creator' God has prompted a deeper desire to embrace and enjoy the freedom and scope for diversity and creativity within worship environments. These corporate worship environments have the potential to be visual, active, sensory, communal, reflective, educational, transformational and gloriously multi-dimensional! (Does that describe your gatherings?) Within this creative landscape, it appears that liturgy is enjoying a bit of a re-brand. Whereas before it may have sounded stuffy and old century, it now has a vibrancy and relevance for all ages and is finding a home within varying styles of expression. Perhaps liturgy is also an antidote for the cultural malaise of shallow being the new deep!!

What?

- Liturgy means the 'work of the people' where we come as one body participating together in confession of sin, adoration, prayer, proclamation of the gospel (preaching), reading Scripture, and sharing the Eucharist (communion).
- Our Worship services should form and shape us into the Body of Christ and not to entertain us, or whip-up some good emotions! Liturgy keeps us from the temptation to be anonymous or treat the meetings as personal experiences that can be kept to ourselves and apart from the rest of the body. We all participate together.
- Narratives, prayers and inter-active meditations pass on Christian tradition and amplify spiritual writings.
- They also help us re-engage with God-truths in the light of our fast-paced changing culture and striking world events…an inter-weaving of past, present and future. For example, this traditional Franciscan blessing is particularly poignant in our current times :

May God bless you with discomfort
at easy answers, half-truths, and superficial relationships

So that you may live from deep within your heart.

May God bless you with anger
at injustice, oppression, and exploitation of God's creations

So that you may work for justice, freedom and peace.

May God bless you with tears to shed for those who suffer pain, rejection, hunger and war,

So that you may reach out your hand to comfort them and to turn their pain into joy.

And may God bless you with just enough foolishness to believe that you can make a difference in the world,

So that you can do what others claim cannot be done:

To bring justice and kindness to all our children and the poor.

When?

- Writer and speaker John Leach, encourages us to use Liturgies "thoughtfully and intentionally".
- They can accompany the sacrament of Communion and they can articulate confession; they can be prayers to express heartfelt longings and intentions and they can illuminate Scripture. They can espouse the great mysteries of the faith and they can proclaim key elements of faith – the creed, the Lord's Prayer, the commandments.
- They can be poetic, interactive, visual, musical, words on a wall, or in the form of installations or a practical exercise to promote an active response. This is where creativity and Liturgy kiss...
- The 'little things' of liturgy are often the most important, in that in doing them consistently, they form us in certain ways. Ultimately, that's what active participation in liturgical worship does: it forms us as the Body of Christ, conforms us to the image of Christ.
- Liturgies invite us to participate, to repeat and to enact. This fuels community response and kicks against independence!
- Finding a liturgical rhythm within the Church Calendar can be meaningful and effective. Helps us not lose the treasure of dates and seasons.
- Prayers and liturgies are emerging out of the worship life of particular communities and released as resources to help others cultivate contemplative and creative liturgical expressions.

So, don't just flip the pages when you see the liturgy… read it and use it!

Sue Rinaldi

A&R Consultant, Elevation Music